Contents

Foreword

Application Specific Integrated Circuits have been in use for two decades. For most of this time they were a specialized and esoteric corner of the semi-conductor marketplace. During the last few years, however, powerful workstations, comprehensive CAD systems and small feature size, silicon gate CMOS logic have conspired to stimulate a rapid growth in their use. ASICs have, today, penetrated almost every technical field and many non-technical ones. They are to be found in activities as disparate as medicine and gambling, music and metrology, graphics and geology. They are infiltrating most engineering disciplines.

There is, therefore, a need for a book which will serve as an introductory text for engineers, for technicians and for physics students. Malcolm Haskard's *An Introduction to Application Specific Integrated Circuits* fulfills that need. It will also be useful to many actual or potential ASIC users with a basic knowledge of electronics—whether or not they expect to develop skills in the design of ASICs.

The book is up-to-date and general. It covers a wide field and embraces programmable logic, gate arrays, standard cell and full custom ASICs. It includes chapters on educational gate arrays, silicon compilers and software.

ASIC usage is evolving through a growth phase towards maturity. At this stage there is more need for information than instruction, more need for astute application than for ingenious design. In this regard the book is very timely for it is written to inform on a general level rather than to teach any specific skills.

New products which exploit ASICs have frequently enjoyed a strong market success. This is a sure indicator of a clear competitive advantage. The advantage must also be of a very general nature because the fields of application have been so wide. It is therefore to the benefit of all that this technology should continue to permeate society. This book, and others like it, has a valuable role to play, both amongst practitioners and users, in fostering and furthering the exploitation of ASICs of all types.

E. S. Eccles

Director and General Manager
Micro Circuit Engineering
Gloucestershire, UK

August 1989

Preface

While application specific integrated circuits (ASICs) are not a new technology, they are becoming the lifeline of electronics. Predicted world growth figures indicate that, for silicon, it is the fastest growing semiconductor area. Further gate arrays, one type of ASICs, are now appearing in gallium arsenide technology. It is therefore important that both industrial and educational establishments come to grips with ASICs. This book provides an introduction to this technology.

The Microelectronics Centre at the South Australian Institute of Technology, and through its commercial arm Australian Silicon Technology, has gained a wealth of experience in integrated circuit design, including ASICs. For example, we established for Australian industry the first truly low-cost gate array service, a service that also employed simple computer aided design techniques that did not require industry to have an in-depth knowledge of silicon technology. This text shares the knowledge and experiences gained over the past twenty years.

A particular concern of mine is training in the area. For most teaching institutions, silicon fabrication is an expensive exercise. Chapter 8 discusses special educational gate arrays that allow individual student exercises to be fabricated at minimum costs.

Special thanks must go to those who, over the years, have assisted me in this work. In particular, Greg Pouferis and Malcolm MacDonald of Australian Silicon Technology, Matthew George of the Microelectronics Centre, John Crawford of Philips Microelectronics, South Australia and Stuart Eccles of Micro Circuit Engineering, United Kingdom.

Finally, it is hoped that this work will encourage industry to make full use of ASIC technology, claiming the advantages it offers, for to ignore it could well mean failure of that industry.

Malcolm R. Haskard
South Australian Institute of Technology
4 August 1988

1 Application specific integrated circuits

1.1 Introduction

Part of the design of a new product employing electronics is to examine and decide on the most appropriate method of manufacture of the electronic component. Figure 1.1 shows the range of manufacturing technologies available.

At one end of the scale there is the printed circuit board (sometimes called printed wiring board) consisting of etched copper tracks separated by insulating layers of laminate. Figure 1.2 shows a printed circuit card. Components are either mounted on the

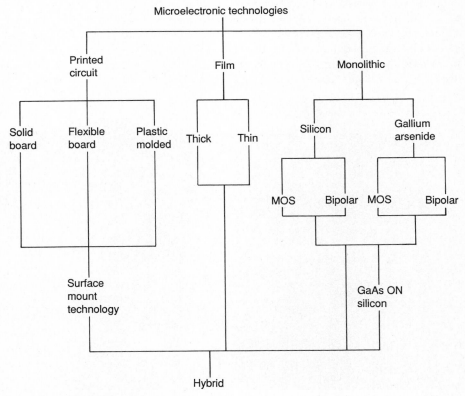

Figure 1.1 Microelectronic technologies

outer surfaces of the board (surface mount technology) or, in the case of leaded components, the leads pass through plated holes in the laminate. In both cases, solder is employed to make an electrical and mechanical connection between the copper track and the component. The printed circuit board may be single or double sided, multilayer, rigid or flexible, contain thermal sinks to remove heat and, more recently, be moulded out of plastic (Ganjei, 1986).

Another family of manufacturing technologies is film. Here, conducting, resistive and insulating (dielectric) layers are deposited in turn on an insulating substrate. The process used to deposit these layers is either a screen printing process, giving rise to what is called thick film, or vacuum deposition techniques called thin film (Haskard 1988).

The most sophisticated of the manufacturing technologies is the monolithic, where devices are fabricated in a semiconducting material such as silicon or gallium arsenide. This process allows the greatest packing densities and today it is possible to produce integrated circuits of over a million transistors.

Finally, there are various techniques that combine two or more of these technologies to achieve a more satisfactory result for a product. These are known as hybrids. Figure 1.3 shows a thick film hybrid module.

In recent years some novel changes have occurred in the monolithic area. Until recently the design of integrated circuits was a very specialist area, only available to large organizations and semiconductor design houses. Today, the design of integrated circuits is a formal part of many engineering degree courses (electrical/electronic/computer engineering) so that more professional people have the skills to design integrated circuits to meet their own requirements. This, coupled with a more open access to foundries has made user specific integrated circuits (USICs) in silicon and now gallium arsenide a reality. Figure 1.4 summarizes the silicon manufacturing alternatives.

Figure 1.2   Printed circuit card unit

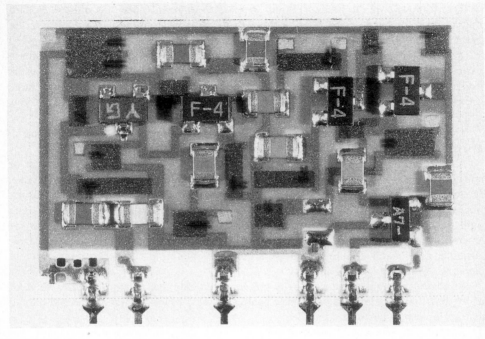

Figure 1.3 Thick film hybrid unit

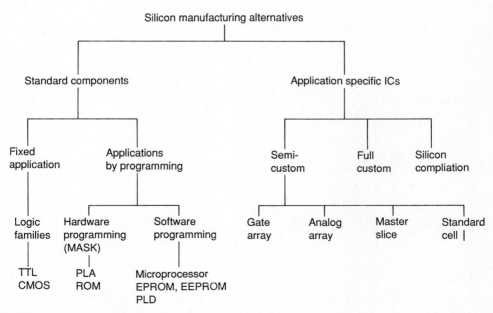

Figure 1.4 Silicon manufacturing alternatives

There are two main streams. First, standard components that are either standard product lines for fixed applications or those that can be programmed. However, it is the second group, namely applications specific integrated circuits (ASICs), that are having the greatest impact on industry. Each integrated circuit is designed specifically for a particular customer application, designed either by staff of the company developing the product, one of the many design houses that have recently been set up or by a large semiconductor house. The semicustom varieties are very attractive in that costs are low, being shared among clients and, further, they can be produced relatively speedily.

There are four types of semicustom circuits and they will be discussed in detail in later chapters. However, a definition for each type will now be given.

A *gate array* is a chip that contains a prediffused but unconnected pattern of gates or gate components. Interconnection of the gates is made by one or more customized masks. Because all the early processing steps to form the gates are the same for all users, processing costs can be shared among gate array users. Since these arrays consist of basic logic gates they are only suitable for digital systems. The designer is responsible for generating the details of the interconnection mask(s) to characterize the array for their particular application. Figure 1.5 shows an experimental chip comparing four different gate array styles.

An *analog array* is again a partially prefabricated chip that contains either a range of analog basic circuit elements or discrete analog devices, which are interconnected into an analog circuit by a customized mask.

Master slice is a combination of the previous two types. It is a prefabricated chip consisting of a mix of gate and analog arrays, allowing systems containing both analog and digital functions to be customized by a mask(s). There will frequently be a range of master slices, to cover systems having different analog circuit requirements. One chip may be simply a gate array with analog to digital and digital to analog converters. Still others may include operational amplifiers, voltage controlled oscillators and comparators for switched capacitors filters as well as a gate array. A variation of all these is the

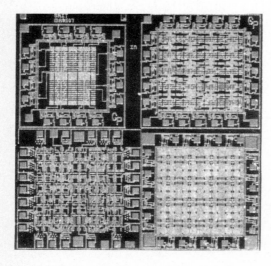

Figure 1.5 An experimental chip to compare four different gate array types

Table 1.2 Typical minimum costs (1988) for establishing a design workstation and fabricating prototype sample (figures are in dollars)

Parameter	PCB	Thick film	PLD	Gate array	Standard cell	Full custom
Processing to prototyping samples	200	500	10–500	2 500	5 000	5 000
Design software on IBM clone	3 000	—	5 000	3 500	5 500	16 000
Design software on major workstation	150 000	150 000	—	200 000	200 000	250 000

of several stages. An initial simulation may verify the correctness of the schematic diagram to achieve the desired functional operation. After automatic layout of the chip, a second simulation will be undertaken. This will include all the standard cell parameters and all parasitic devices and will give a true indication of the final chip performance including timing.

Having designed and even fabricated a chip, there is the problem of testing it. Again this is normally undertaken during the design phase using computer techniques. An output from the simulation runs is to produce a set of test vectors, so that full functional and timing testing can be carried out after the chips are packaged.

Since it is impractical to design ASICs without computer aided design, what are the likely costs involved in purchasing a computer workstation and software? Again prices vary considerably from vendor to vendor, and it will also depend on the size and type of ASIC selected. Table 1.2 provides typical minimum costs for design software, workstation and processing costs. For many applications, the low-cost IBM clone workstation is adequate. Processing time is longer, but often this is not considered a hardship. Where an expensive workstation is obtained (Sun, Mentor Graphics, Daisy, Hewlett Packard, Tektronics, etc.) the station can be shared with other projects, for example drafting, layout of printed circuit boards, and so forth. Naturally there could be some increased software costs to enable these operations to be undertaken.

1.4 Future predictions

Bob Gottliebsen (1985) when talking about how new microelectronic technology is changing business said, 'the rate of change coming . . . the next ten years is likely to make the last twenty years look as if we have stood still'. Microelectronics and, in particular, ASICs is not only a powerful enabling technology, but is pervasive so that no area escapes. It will allow new products to be generated and the old to be upgraded; it will transform production methods, including the very design methodology used to generate the product. Keith Lobo (1987) of LSI Logic believes that most future electronic systems will be complex ASICs and standard memory. There will be no microprocessors or glue chips. Microprocessors will be simply macro library cells.

Table 1.3 shows the predicted world market figures for several silicon technologies. It shows that the major growth area will be that of the ASICs. Sir John Clark, Chairman of

Table 1.3   Predicted world market figure in 1000 million dollars (US)

Item	1986	1990/91	Beyond 1991
Total logic semiconductors	7.1	15.5	
PLD	0.3	1.1	
ASIC—gate array	1.8	2.5	
ASIC—standard cell	0.5	5.5	
ASIC share of total	32%	50%	60–80%

Plessey says, 'ASICs are growing at the rate of 50 percent per year and it will account for nearly 70 percent of the worldwide semiconductor market in the mid 1990s' (Fletcher, 1988). It is apparent then that all industry must come to grips with ASICs, for to ignore them and their effects will mean failure.

1.5   Questions

1. As the engineer you are required to recommend to management the microelectronic process that should be used for the latest product.
   List the factors that you consider important in making the decision.
2. Silicon microelectronics is an all-pervasive technology and application specific integrated circuits are making major inroads into every discipline. For example:
   > agriculture: implanted chips to identify individual animals
   > mining: electronic detonators for precise timing.
   Draw up a list of key disciplines/industries and then find out one example for each where ASICs have made a major contribution.
3. Explain the difference between a gate array and a standard cell integrated circuit.
4. Keith Lobo of LSI Logic believes that most future electronic systems will be complex ASICs and standard memory. There will be no microprocessor or glue chips. Microprocessors will be simply a macro library cell. If true, what impact do you think this will have on industry?

1.6   Bibliography

Fletcher, P. (1988). 'Plessey faces a tough job in its chip business', *Electronics,* vol. 61, 7 Jan., p.43–4.

Ganjei, J. (1986). 'Mould your own', *Circuits and Manufacturing*, vol. 26, June, p.39–50.

Gottliebsen, B. (1985). 'How new technology is changing business', *Technological Change.* Impact of Information Technology, National Information Technology Council Inc., Australia.

Haskard, M. R. (1988). 'Thick film hybirds: Manufacture and design', Prentice Hall, N.Y.

Hoover, Jr, C. W. Harrod, W. L. & Cohen, M. I. (1987). 'The technology of interconnection', *AT & T Technical Journal*, vol. 66, no. 4, p.2–12.

Lobo. K. (1987). 'Semicustom today and tomorrow', *VLSI System Design*, vol. 8, 20 May. p.28–9.

Waller, L. (1987). 'Can big chip houses make it in ASICs?', *Electronics*, vol. 60, 6 August, p.60–4.

2 Technologies

2.1 Introduction

Over the years there have been numerous technologies proposed and used for producing integrated circuits. Figure 2.1 shows a selection of processes. As can be seen there are many variations and it is almost impossible to include them all on a single diagram. For example, trench isolation may be employed to improve packing density. BICMOS processes are a combined bipolar and CMOS process to enhance the performance of

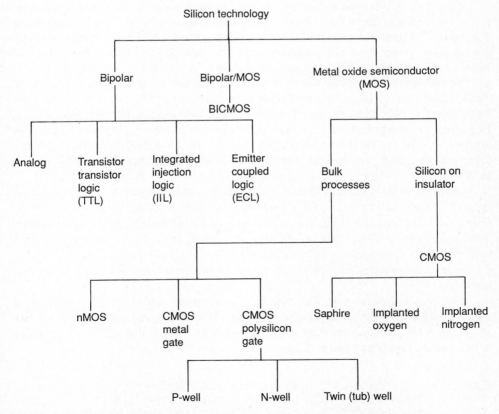

Figure 2.1 Selection of silicon processes used to make integrated circuits

11

analog circuits on a CMOS chip. In this section we will concentrate on the two basic processes, namely, a simple bipolar and a P-well bulk CMOS process, for this will provide a simple yet adequate foundation. It must be pointed out that most foundries producing ASICs will employ their own variations on these basic processes. A product manufacturer wishing to have a more detailed understanding of a particular process should consult the foundry direct. As we will see later such detailed knowledge is not usually required.

2.2   Logic families

There are today some five popular logic families still in use and they are shown in Figure 2.2. Considering first the bipolar circuits, there are three:

1. Transistor transistor logic (TTL);
2. Emitter coupled logic (ECL); and
3. Integrated injection logic (IIL).

While TTL is still widely used in standard product ranges, its popularity as a logic circuit for ASICs is declining. It can be produced in various forms giving low-power to high-speed versions; however, it has largely been superseded by CMOS processes which have a lower power consumption and a greater packing density. Some gate arrays still exist. Foundries even use TTL gate arrays to extend their standard product ranges.

The ECL circuit is popular where very fast circuits are needed. Circuits operating at clock frequencies of some hundreds of MHz are available. The disadvantage is large dissipation and only medium sized ASICs are presently available. The final bipolar type, IIL, offers extremely high packing densities, very low power consumption, but at low frequencies, that is, less than 1 MHz clock frequencies. Even though an IIL circuit can operate from supply voltages as low as 1 volt, its use has been eroded by CMOS technology.

For the metal oxide semiconductor (MOS) process there are two fundamental circuit types: N-channel MOS (nMOS) and complementary MOS (CMOS) where both P- and N-channel devices are used. While the nMOS process is considerably simpler, it consumes more power than a CMOS process. Further, it is easier to produce analog circuits in a CMOS process. Consequently the use of the nMOS process is declining.

Figure 2.3 compares the speed and power requirements of the five logic families discussed.

From this discussion it is seen that the process most commonly used for general purpose ASICs is CMOS. The bipolar ECL and IIL processes are employed to a lesser extent when the particular application cannot be met by CMOS, that is high speed (ECL) or low voltage supply and power (IIL).

Figure 2.2   Common logic families used for ASICs. Bipolar families: (a) transistor transistor logic (TTL); (b) emitter coupled logic (ECL); (c) integrated injection logic (IIL) or merged transistor logic (MTL). MOS families; (d) n channel MOS (nMOS); (e) complementary MOS (CMOS)

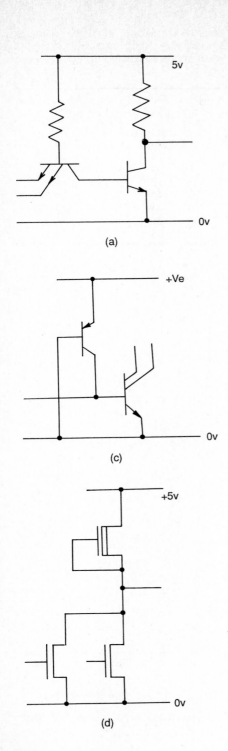

(a)

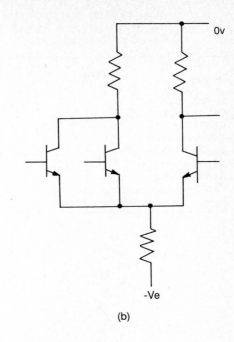

(b)

(c)

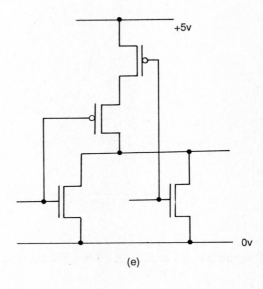

(d)

(e)

Table 2.1   Use of ASICs. Figures are the numbers of responses from the sample. They give an indication of what designers are doing and predictions of what they may be doing in the future. A blank indicates no figures were given in the report

Process	1985	Year 1987	1989
CMOS gate array	32	53	46
CMOS standard cell	17	35	34
CMOS compiled	—	17	29
nMOS standard cell	14	—	—
Bipolar standard cell	15	12	—
ECL gate array	13	14	16
GaAs gate array	—	5	23
CMOS programmable logic devices	8	26	36
Bipolar programmable logic devices	27	25	16

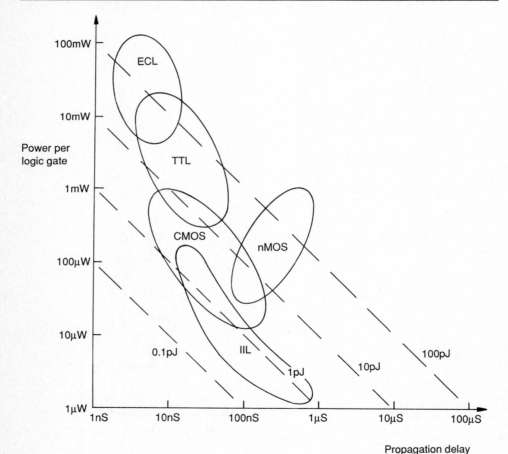

Figure 2.3   Comparison of the speed and power performance of the five logic families

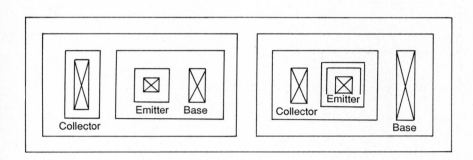

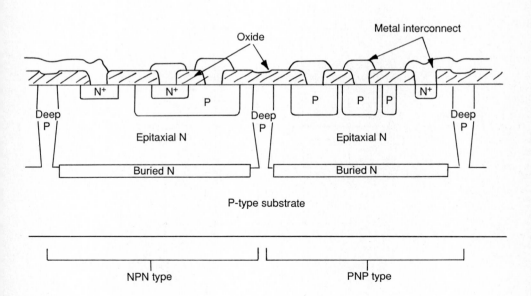

Figure 2.7 Bipolar transistor construction showing vertical NPN and lateral PNP types

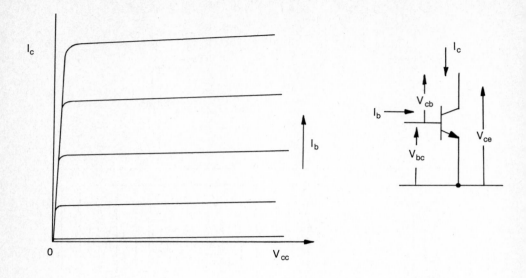

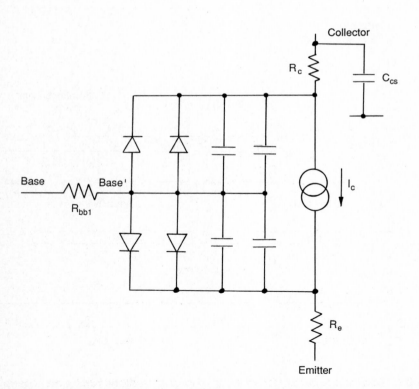

Figure 2.8 Static characteristics and model for a bipolar transistor

Table 2.3   Typical bipolar transistor parameters

Parameter	NPN	PNP	Units
α_N	0.996	0.8	—
α_I	0.2	0.01	—
I_{beo}	1.10^{-15}	1.10^{-15}	A
I_{cbo}	1.10^{-6}	1.10^{-8}	A

Equations that model the current in a bipolar transistor are (Haskard & May, 1987):

$$I_c = \alpha_N I_{beo} \left(e^{\frac{qV_{be}}{kT}} - 1 \right) + I_{cbo} \left(e^{\frac{qV_{cb}}{kT}} - 1 \right) \qquad [2.3]$$

$$I_e = I_{beo} \left(e^{\frac{qV_{be}}{kT}} - 1 \right) + \alpha_I I_{cbo} \left(e^{\frac{qV_{cb}}{kT}} - 1 \right) \qquad [2.4]$$

where I_c and I_e are the collector and emitter currents respectively
   I_{beo} is the base emitter diode reverse leakage current with the collector open circuit
   I_{cbo} is the collector base diode reverse leakage current with the emitter open circuit
   V_{be} and V_{cb} are the base emitter and collector diode respective voltages
   α_N is the normal common base current gain
   α_I is the inverse common base current gain
   k is Boltzmann's constant
   T is the temperature in K

Figure 2.8 shows the common emitter static characteristics for an NPN transistor and a suitable model for an analog simulation program. Typical parameter values are given in Table 2.3.

2.4   Manufacturing technologies

Integrated circuits are built up layer by layer, using a mask for each layer to define the area to which processing is restricted. The transfer of the mask information can be achieved by one of several methods. A resist is spun onto the wafer and exposed to ultraviolet light through the mask. Developing of the resist allows portions to be washed away, exposing the wafer underneath for processing. An alternative method is to write directly onto the resist with a laser or electron beam. Again, after developing the resist the selected areas are washed away. This process is called photo or electron beam lithography. An alternative name is patterning.

For many of the processing steps, a layer of silicon dioxide is thermally grown or spun onto the top of the wafer and is used as a protective layer. To process the silicon beneath, the oxide layer must be removed. After carrying out the lithography process, the silicon dioxide, where now exposed, is etched away using a hydrofluoric acid solution. Figure 2.9 shows this for the photolithographic process.

Other processing steps used are:

1. ion implantation, where selected impurity ions are 'fired' into the silicon using an electrostatic accelerator then annealed to form P and N doped regions;
2. polysilicon deposition employing a chemical vapor deposition process;
3. silicon dioxide growth using thermal (both wet and dry) methods;
4. metalization where aluminum and/or other materials are deposited under vacuum conditions;
5. selective etching of layers using dry plasma and/or wet chemical methods.

Figure 2.10 shows these processes combined to produce a CMOS inverter circuit (Figure 2.11). Some eight masks are required for this process. First, a protective silicon

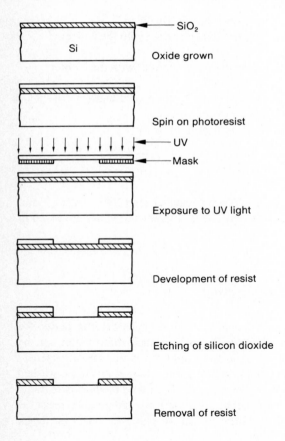

Si

SiO$_2$

Oxide grown

Spin on photoresist

UV

Mask

Exposure to UV light

Development of resist

Etching of silicon dioxide

Removal of resist

Figure 2.9   The patterning process

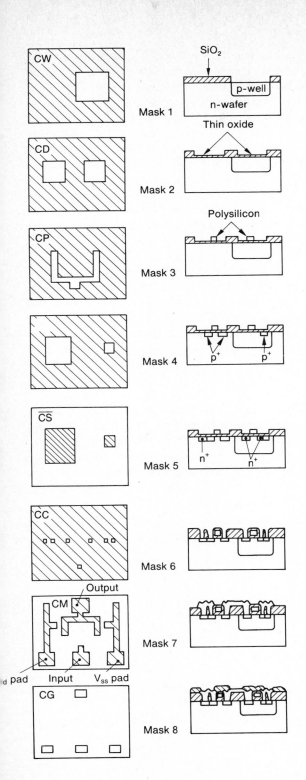

Figure 2.10
Steps in a P-well CMOS process to produce the inverter circuit given in Figure 2.11

dioxide layer is thermally grown. It is called the field oxide and is typically 0.5 to 1 micron thick. Using the P-well mask (CW) the areas where the wells are to be placed are opened up. Using ion implantation, the P-well is formed. After annealing, the oxide layer is regrown over the wafer. Using the second mask (CD) an oxide wash is carried out to thin it to the required gate oxide thickness ($\approx 800\text{Å}$) where the transistors are to be formed. Polysilicon is then deposited over the wafer and using mask 3 (CP), selectively etched, leaving the two transistor gate areas. Next P and N source/diffusion areas are implanted through the thin oxide using masks 4 and 5. For contacts to be made, the field oxide layer is etched using mask 6 (CC). Metal, usually aluminum, is deposited over the whole wafer and selectively etched using mask 7 (CM) to leave the required inter-connections. Finally a glaze of silicon dioxide is spun onto the wafer as a protective coating and etched away from the pad areas so that connections can be made from the pads to the package. Mask 8 (CG) is used in this step.

At this point the wafer processing is finished. Although Figure 2.10 shows only a single circuit, it must be remembered that there are many hundreds of these circuits manufactured simultaneously across the surface of the wafer. The wafer may range in diameter from 100 to 200 mm (4 to 8 inches) whereas each chip may only be several tens of square millimetres in area. Figure 2.12 shows a wafer after processing in the foundry.

After fabrication the wafer is usually inspected and then automatically probed, that is, simple static tests are made and faulty circuits marked with an inker. The wafer is then sawn into the individual circuits called dice, die or chips and the good ones are packaged. Final tests are then carried out to ensure all the devices sold meet the customer's requirements.

Figure 2.13 summarizes the overall processing stages for a gate array system. On the left-hand side there is the wafer processing right up to the final characterization stage. The right-hand side shows the design process to produce the characterization layer information. The two are combined in a characterizing patterning process shown here as a direct writing electron beam lithographic process. The required metalization is then formed by developing and etching. Wafers are tested, sawn, packaged and then the individual integrated circuits undergo a final acceptance test.

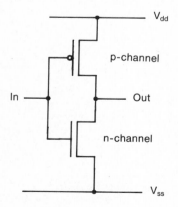

Figure 2.11   Simple CMOS inverter circuit

2.5 Product complexity and quality

The complexity of integrated circuits has increased rapidly, initially doubling every year (Moore's Law). Recently there has been a slowing down, caused by problems associated with the interconnection of transistors to form circuits. Figure 2.14 shows the growth in complexity for both silicon and gallium arsenide circuits employing field effect transistors. Because of the isolation areas needed for bipolar transistors, the complexity of bipolar circuits are at least an order less. This increase in complexity is partly due to the larger chip sizes that can now be fabricated and partly due to the shrinking of device dimensions—both the result of fabrication improvements. Figure 2.15 shows the reduction in dimensions, with time, for silicon MOS transistors. Thus present day integrated circuits can be extremely complex, containing many thousands of transistors and, in order to obtain both high processing yields and reliable chips, special quality assurance and control procedures must be employed. For example the five specially inserted test die shown in Figure 2.12 allow the monitoring of fabrication steps and extraction of process parameters.

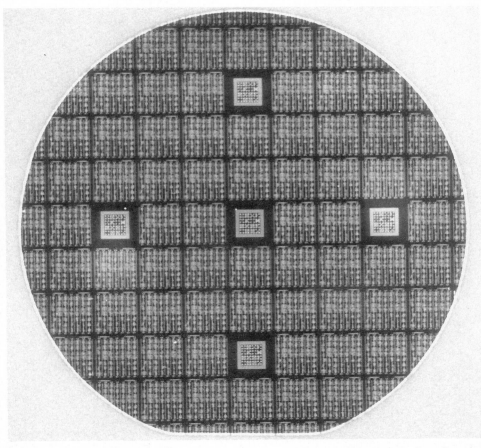

Figure 2.12 Completed wafer after foundry processing and before being diced

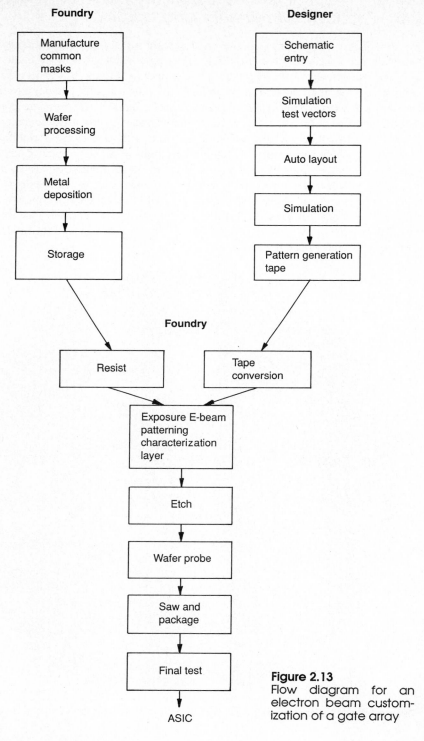

Figure 2.13
Flow diagram for an electron beam customization of a gate array

Table 3.1 Functions to be generated by a universal logic circuit

Input		Outputs															
A	B	0	1	2	3	4	5	6	7	8	9	10	11	12	13	14	15
		0	$\overline{A+B}$	$\overline{A}B$	$\overline{A}$	$A\overline{B}$	$\overline{B}$	$A\overline{B}+\overline{A}B$	$\overline{AB}$	AB	$\overline{AB}$+$\overline{A}\overline{B}$	B	$\overline{A}+B$	A	$A+\overline{B}$	$\overline{A}+B$	1
0	0	0	1	0	1	0	1	0	1	0	1	0	1	0	1	0	1
0	1	0	0	1	1	0	0	1	1	0	0	1	1	0	0	1	1
1	0	0	0	0	0	1	1	1	1	0	0	0	0	1	1	1	1
1	1	0	0	0	0	0	0	0	0	1	1	1	1	1	1	1	1

1. What logic/gate configuration to use?
2. How many pads are required?
3. What is the best layout of the gates or floor plan to provide adequate signal routing and power distribution?

   We will briefly consider these in turn.

3.2.1 Logic gates

The logic gate that is used must be one that is compact and flexible in that it can be easily combined to produce many different logic functions. The ideal situation is for a universal logic circuit (May, Haskard and Bannigan, 1983). Table 3.1 shows the functions that need to be generated by a universal logic circuit for two logic inputs A and B. There are 16 functions possible. Of these only 12 are of any value since functions 0 and 15 are useless,

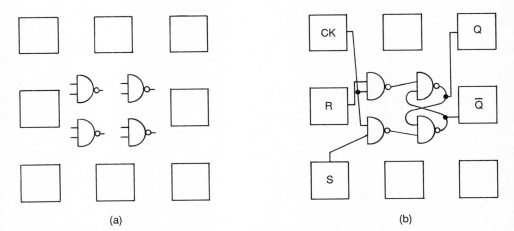

Figure 3.1 The gate array concept: (a) uncharacterized array and (b) final characterized array to perform the customer's required logic function

while 10 and 12 are equal to the inputs. However, if the latter two are retained, it can be seen that these 14 functions consist of 7 pairs with one member of each pair being the complement of the other. Using this property, only 7 functions are required if complementary signals are also generated.

Figure 3.2 shows a simple nMOS universal logic cell. It needs to be configured for each function using the characterization mask. Unfortunately the number of signal interconnection wires poses a severe routing problem, as both normal and complement signals often need to be routed. The source impedances are also important for the circuit given. The logic signals A1 and A2 must be from low impedance sources, while logic signals B1 and B2 can be from either low or high impedance sources.

Simpler cells employing fewer transistors turn out to be almost as flexible. For example, Figure 3.3 shows a 4-transistor cell that can perform four 3-input logic functions. Unfortunately, most engineers have been conditioned to think in terms of Boolean expressions and the more complex functions (other than NOR and NAND) are seldom used. Thus it is usually more efficient to employ a standard minimum device NOR or NAND circuit.

For the original arrays the layout of this basic gate cell was done as a square configuration, so that with a logic connection into or out of the cell placed in each corner, four connections were possible, for example, a 3-input NAND or NOR cell or a 2-input NAND/AND or NOR/OR cell.

This particular layout (Figure 3.4) becomes inefficient when power distribution and routing between cells is considered. Grouping cells into four is more efficient, but this limits each cell to three connections (Figure 3.4(b)), that is 2-input NAND or NOR circuits.

This is the simplest type of gate array cell, and arrays employing more complex gate structures are often expressed in terms of the number of equivalent 2-input gates.

Today the majority of gate arrays employ CMOS where the usual configuration is a mixture of 2-input and 3-input gates. Normally transistors are left unconnected so that the characterization mask determines whether the circuit is connected as a NAND or a NOR gate. Figure 3.5 shows a typical CMOS gate cell.

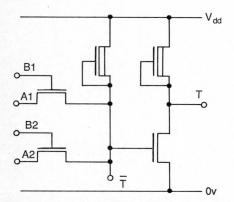

Figure 3.2   An nMOS 5-transistor universal logic cell

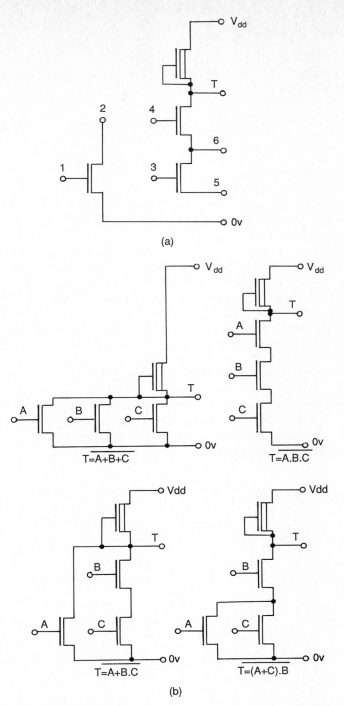

Figure 3.3 A 4-transistor nMOS logic gate (a) that can achieve up to four 3-input logic functions (b)

3.2.2 Number of pads

The next problem is the number of pads and types that are required for a gate array. Rent's rule (Laudman and Russo, 1971) gives for random logic a relationship between the number of pads needed and the number of cells.

$$P = kC^r \qquad\qquad [3.1]$$

where P is the number of pads

C is the number of logic cells

k is the number of input/output connections per cell

r is an exponent $0.45 \le r \le 1$ and for integrated circuits r is typically 0.6.

This rule is used as a guide to determine the number of pads, but in the final analysis the actual number is set by pad size and the length of the chip periphery.

Since Rent's rule does not evaluate the ratio of input to output pads, for that depends upon the particular logic expression being implemented, each pad is normally designed so that it can be configured as an input or output pad. Tristate output pads can also be designed, but these consume more area as additional components are required. Larger pads means fewer of them for the same silicon area. Consequently the various manufacturers offer different solutions. Some produce gate arrays with no tristate outputs, others with all pads being able to be configured for tristate output while still others a mixture of the two—for example, 12 of the 48 pads being able to be connected as a tristate output. Another variation is whether or not the control line to place the output pad into the high impedance state is common to all of the tristate output pads. Figure 3.6 shows the layout for a gate array pad.

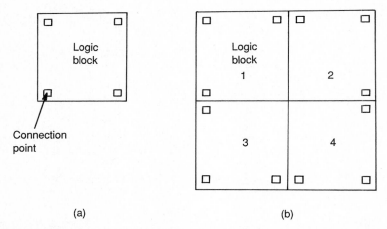

(a)   (b)

Figure 3.4 Logic block configurations: (a) single cell per block; (b) four cells per block

3.2.3 Layout

The amount of room that is left for routing is probably the most critical parameter of all. If too much silicon is left, then the number of gates is reduced, while if too little routing area is provided, then gate utilization will be poor as there will be gates that cannot be connected. Work undertaken at IBM (Heller et al., 1977) has given some guidelines as to how much area should be left. Up to 75 percent of a chip area can be required for routing, leaving only 25 percent of the silicon occupied by gates.

There are today three basic approaches in organizing a floor plan for a gate array. These are shown in Figure 3.7. First, the island or block approach was originally used. The corners of the blocks often had underpasses built into them so that the interconnection wires could cross. Figure 3.8 shows such a block cell layout in nMOS technology.

The next development was the row floor plan where the logic inputs and outputs flow vertically through a cell and can be interconnected at either the top, bottom or both. Dummy feed throughs can be placed in some cells or between cells. Figure 3.9 shows the layout of such a cell.

The final organization shown in Figure 3.7 is an entirely different approach and was only made possible through having multiple metalization for interconnections. Here gates are placed all over the chip (sea of gates) and the interconnections run over the whole of the surface. Gates under a wiring lane may not be able to be connected, but this does not matter. If more gates are needed then a chip with a greater number of gates is selected.

Of these three methods the row approach is the predominant floor plan for small gate arrays, while the sea of gates is employed for very large gate arrays. Using automatic routing methods, it is seldom that 100 percent gate utilization is achieved, 75–80 percent being common. Should there be insufficient number of gates available to complete a design, then manual intervention may take place, or an array with a larger number of gates on it selected.

3.2.4 Technology

Turning now to the technology used in gate arrays, the most common type is CMOS. Depending on speed requirements, arrays in 5 microns through to submicron technologies are available. Where very high speed performance is required, silicon ECL or gallium arsenide arrays are available with clock speeds over 1 GHz. Characterization of the array depends on the number of layers of metallization used and may need from one to five masks. In the simplest case, the single mask characterizes the final metalization layer, defining the interconnect paths. Where additional masks are needed, it is to make contact cuts in insulating layers, define one or more metal layer interconnection patterns, and possibly a final overglaze pattern.

To speed up processing, a range of novel techniques has been developed by some foundries. These include electron beam (Texas Instruments, 1987) and laser beam (Cole, 1987) direct write on the wafer. The first provides a turn-around time of a week; while the latter, hours. It has even been suggested that clean room trucks may call at plant doors and, using laser technology characterize gate arrays for a client in a few hours on site. Yet another innovation is the potential to modify ASIC designs using electron beams (Electronics, 1988).

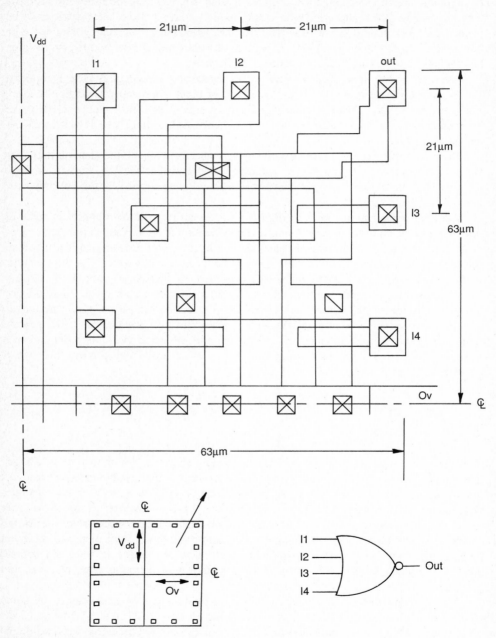

Figure 3.8   Block gate array cell layout

Channel

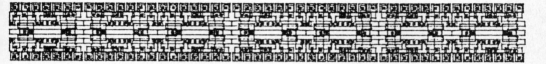

Channel

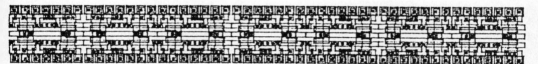

Figure 3.9 Row cell specification showing where interconnections can be made

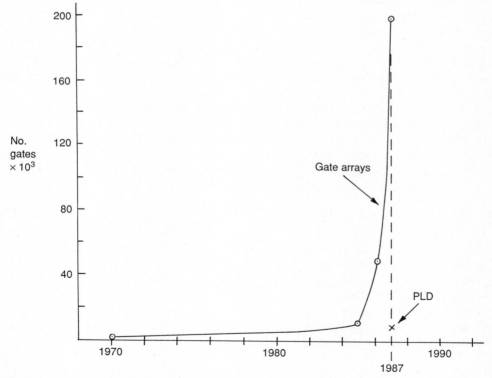

Figure 3.10 Growth in gate array size available

In parallel with these developments has been the exponential growth in gate array size and the availability of user friendly support software. Figure 3.10 shows the rate of growth in the maximum number of gates on an array. The number of gate array vendors listed in the US (Sources VLSI Design) has increased from 21 in 1984 to over 60 in 1987. All this suggests that gate arrays are a fast, cost efficient method of transferring electronic systems from ideas into hardware.

3.3   Analog arrays

Many electronic systems need to interface with the real or physical world. Since the real world is analog, analog as well as digital circuits are often required. Thus, in recent years there has been an effort to provide analog ASICs as well as digital. It was natural that digital methods should come first as the simplicity of a two-state circuit allows it to be easily designed and fabricated using silicon processes that have production spreads on parameters often as large as 50–200 percent. Programs to simulate analog circuits are more complex and consume more computer time, while stability problems arising from having high-gain amplifiers in such close proximity on a chip, all point to analog circuits being more difficult, and therefore they were initially put to one side.

In reality, simple analog arrays did appear very early on the scene, about the same time as the early gate arrays; however, they never really took off as an idea. These analog arrays consisted of a number of discrete bipolar devices, transistors, resistors, diodes, etc., and the designer had to interconnect them with a metalization mask to form the amplifiers, oscillators, filters, and so forth. There were no library of layouts or software support. It was a manual trial and error process. All of this is changing. Manufacturers of analog arrays now provide libraries of layouts and a much wider range of devices on the chip.

Analog arrays can be divided into two classes: those with complete function cells and others with subcells. With the first, the chip contains an array of analog function blocks such as operational amplifiers, unity gain buffer amplifiers, capacitors and switches for switched capacitor filters and gain setting, voltage controlled oscillators, voltage references, analog to digital and digital to analog converters. The library contains detailed information on each block and interconnection material illustrating how various functions can be achieved.

Subcells used in the second class of analog arrays are building blocks from which a range of functions can be made up. For example, a differential pair amplifier stage can be combined with an output buffer stage to form a simple operational amplifier. While this approach offers greater flexibility and the potential for greater silicon area utilization, problems such as stability and poor high frequency performance can often occur. A library showing how basic functions can be constructed from the building blocks is normally supplied by the vendor.

Figure 3.11 shows the layout of an analog array chip. It consists of blocks of discrete transistors, resistors and capacitors.

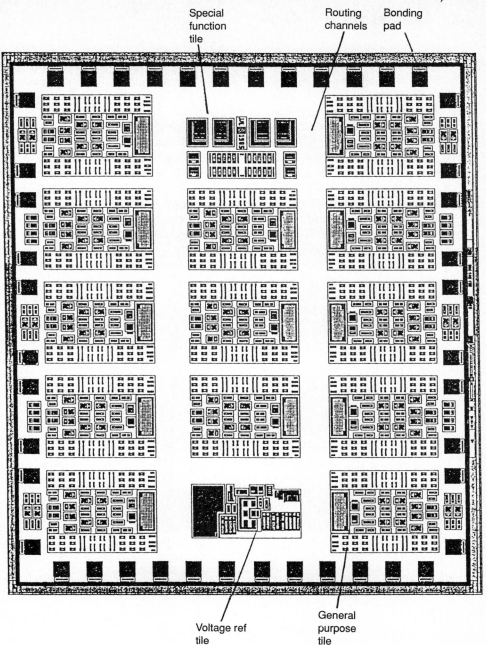

Special
function
tile

Routing
channels

Bonding
pad

Voltage ref
tile

General
purpose
tile

Figure 3.11   Analog array chip (*Micro Linear*)

3.4   Master slice

Many digital control and instrumentation systems must interface with the real or physical world, which is analog and they therefore consist of digital and analog sections (Figure 3.12). While separate gate and analog array chips can be used, there are cost advantages if only a single chip is employed. One class of master slice contains a gate array and a range of analog circuits. Figure 3.13 shows such a chip.

In order to cover the requirements of customers, a range of master slices is produced providing different ratios between the amount of digital to analog circuitry, the type of analog circuitry (e.g. operational amplifiers only, or analog to digital and digital to analog converters) and the size of the gate array. Some master slice integrated circuits are totally digital in that they provide other than logic functions. The most common ones include on chip random access memory (RAM) and/or read only memory (ROM).

Whichever type is required, the design strategy is the same as for a gate array. A schematic diagram is produced calling upon the library cells. The chip is then laid out either manually or automatically by overlaying the analog or digital function blocks on appropriate segments of the chip and then routing the interconnection wires. Methods to achieve this will be discussed more in Chapter 6.

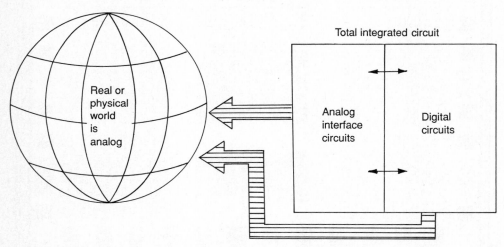

Figure 3.12   The need for combined analog and digital functions on a chip frequently occurs in control and instrumentation systems

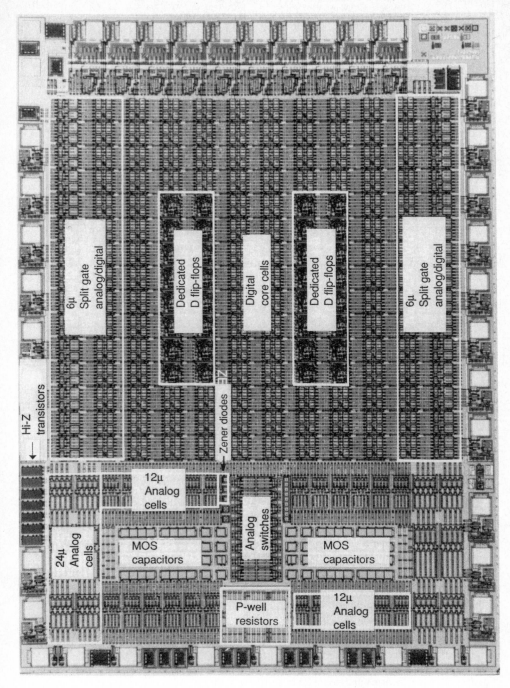

Figure 3.13 Master slice chip consisting of gate and analog array areas (*Universal Semiconductors*)

3.5   Selecting an array

There are many organizations offering a variety of array services. What are the criteria that should be used to select an array and vendor? Four criteria are important:

1. service offered
2. technical specification of the array
3. cost
4. second sourcing.

By far the most important is the quality and speed of the service that is offered. For the novice, a local vendor is probably essential so help can be immediate. It is also important that the vendor be involved in the design right from the outset. A local vendor simplifies this process. The size of the library, range and sophistication of the software are also important. Most software today accepts a schematic entry and from then on the chip is designed automatically with little human intervention. Finally, the time required by the foundry to produce both prototype and later production ASICs must be appropriate. Before committing oneself to a vendor, all of these matters must be sorted out, for once a commitment is made it is too late to turn back.

The technical specifications of the array are naturally important. This includes the size of the arrays, functions offered, pad numbers, speed of operation, package range, and so forth. If, for example, there are large intervals between the sizes of gate arrays, then a much larger chip may be needed, leading to wasted silicon and an unnecessary cost factor. For example, a system needing 900 gates is too large for a 1000 gate array chip (typical gate utilization with automatic routing is 75–80 percent) and so it must be placed on the next size array of 2500 gates. Here the gate utilization will only be 36 percent.

Another important technical consideration is the speed of operation. Most gate array prototypes perform the required function, but up to a third may have the timing or speed incorrect. Thus the selection of a satisfactory array and correctness of timing simulation is very important. Naturally this assumes that the timing/speed requirements described in the product manufacturer's original design specification are correct.

The next criteria is the cost. While the above two factors will have a bearing on the cost of the ASIC, there are many others. For example, the size of the run, the number of attempts to get the design correct, the up front costs to produce the first prototype. This is often called the non-return engineering (NRE) cost.

Finally there could be the important consideration of second sourcing. Its relevance depends on the expected life of the product. For products that are either low cost or have a short life, having a second source may not be important. Here speed of service and costs are the critical parameters. With more expensive long-life products, second sourcing is important. In the early days of gate arrays it was difficult to achieve this, as each foundry had its own particular product and organizations were often forced to work with two different foundries and design two chips. Today, many of the large foundries work together sharing libraries and second sourcing each other.

In a recent survey of ASIC users, the six factors that were considered to be the most important were (Waller 1987):

	Percentage of responses
Prototype works first time	65
Quick prototype turn around time	62
High performance	49
Low cost integrated circuits	49
High density	46
Low development cost	28

3.6   Questions

1. Gates in the center of an array having unused inputs must have those inputs correctly tied to either a 'high' or 'low' state. Special 'tie off' circuits are used and an example is given in Figure 3.14. Verify that it generates the levels indicated. Can you devise an alternative circuit?
2. With reference to Figure 3.5, how can the group of three pairs of CMOS transistors be connected as:
(a) a 3-input NOR gate?
(b) a 3-input NAND gate?
If a 3-input OR gate is needed, how would you employ the remaining CMOS pair of transistors to achieve inversion?
3. A new gate array chip is being designed. It will consist of 1000, 3-input NOR/NAND gates. Estimate the desirable number of pads that the chip should have.
4. Explain the concept of 'sea of gates'. How are the gates interconnected to form a system?
5. What factors do you consider important when selecting an analog array vendor for a new product?

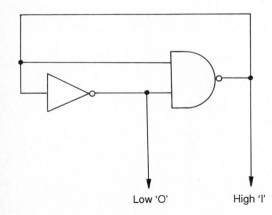

Low 'O'   High 'I'   **Figure 3.14**

3.7   Bibliography

Cole, C. B. (1987). 'Gate arrays big problem! They take too long to build', *Electronics*, vol. 60, 12 November, p.69–74.

Electronics (1988). Products Newsletter, 'Ion-beam system handles ASIC design changes without need to make new mask', *Electronics*, vol.61, 26 May, p.28.

Heller, W. R., Mikhail, W. F. & Donath, W. T. (1977). 'Predictions of wiring space requirements for LSI', *14th Design Automation Conference Proceedings*, p.32–42.

Laudman, B. S. & Russo, R. L. (1971). 'On a pin versus block relationship for partitions of logic graphs', *Trans IEEE on Computers*, vol.C-20, p.1469–79.

May, I. C., Haskard, M. R. & Bannigan, J. T. (1983). 'A MOS uncommitted logic array', *Journal of Electrical and Electronic Engineering Australia*, vol. 3, March, p.48–52.

Texas Instruments (1987). 'E-beam gate array customisation', *Product sheet*, S/C Rev.17, Bedford, UK.

Waller, L. (1987). 'Can big chip houses make it in ASICs?', *Electronics*, vol. 60, 6 August, p.60–4.

3.8   Selected vendors' material

Cherry Semiconductors Corporation (1985). *Semicustom Circuit Design*, East Greenwich, USA.

Linear Technology Inc. (1985). *Semicustom Array Design Manual*, Ontario, Canada.

Micro Circuit Engineering (1986). *Falcon Gate Array Services*, Tewkesbury, UK.

Micro Linear Corporation (1988). *Tile Array Family Users Handbook*, California, USA.

NCR Corporation (1987). *ASIC Data Book*, Ohio, USA.

Philips Industries Ltd. (1987). 'System gate and system cell', *Document No. 9398 338 10011*, Eindhoven, Netherlands.

Texas Instruments (1985).*HCMOS Gate Arrays: TAHC Family Design Manual*, Bedford, UK.

Texas Instruments (1987). 'ASIC Users Guide', *Document No. SCL91-01/87*, Bedford, UK.

3.9   Selected array suppliers

Company	Gate array	Analog Array/Master Slice
AMD/MMI	√	
AMCC	√	
Cherry	√	
Fujitsu	√	
Gain Electronic Corporation	√ (GaAs)	
GE/RCA	√	
Gigabit Logic	√ (GaAs)	
Gould/AMI	√	
Harris	√	
Hitachi	√	
LSI Logic	√	

Linear Technology Inc		√
Micro Circuit Engineering	√	
Micro Linear Corporation		√
Motorola	√	
National/Fairchild	√	
NCR	√	
NEC	√	
Philips/Signetics	√	
Plessey/Ferranti	√	
Raytheon	√	
Semi Process Inc	√	
Siemens	√	
Texas Instruments	√	
Thomson/SGS	√	√
Toshiba	√	√
TriQuint	√ (GaAs)	
Univeral Semiconductors	√	√
Vitesse Semiconductor Corporation	√ (GaAs)	
VLSI Technology	√	

4   Standard cells

4.1   Introduction

A frequent problem with array structures is the amount of silicon that has to be left to cover all possible routing combinations. Thus up to 75 percent of chip area may be left for routing, leaving only 25 percent for gates/analog circuit functions. Another difficulty is circuit utilization. The arrays come in standard sizes and a customer's design must be accommodated on one of those sizes. Gate utilization may be as low as 50 percent so there is again wasted silicon area. With the standard cell approach, the system required is mapped directly onto the silicon, selecting from the library only those function blocks needed and placing them to minimize the routing area. Both analog and digital functions can be included on the chip. Thus the resulting design is considerably more compact than an array and because of reduced stray routing capacities there is a speed improvement.

The penalty for this is increased cost, as there is no inherent sharing of processing costs. However, because the final chips are smaller, there is a cost advantage for large production runs (Figure 1.7). Some mask manufacturers have the capability of merging designs to form a multi-project wafer, so that up to four different chips can be made simultaneously on a single wafer. In such cases there is a sharing of processing costs, but each customer only receives one quarter of the chips from each wafer. This is a useful technique for reducing the cost of supplying prototypes, but not necessarily larger production quantities.

4.2   Design philosophy

The design concept of a standard cell chip is to have a range of standard cells in a library that can be interconnected to build up the required system. There are two basic approaches. The first is called channelled cells where there are alternate rows of cells and routing channels. More recently, with the advent of three or more layers of interconnect metalization, there are the channel-less types where the whole chip area is covered with cells, the routing occurring above them in the top two layers of interconnect metal. A standard XY type routing algorithm can be employed to make the interconnection, with one of the two metal layers used for wires in the X direction and the other for wires in the Y direction. It should be noted that these upper two layers of interconnection metal cannot be used in the construction of the cells.

Both of these methods rely on cells having certain standard characteristics. They are designed to be of a fixed height with variable width, having power rails positioned so that power connection automatically occurs when two cells abut. Input and output lines are also on a grid so that the automatic routing algorithms are simplified. Figure 4.1 shows the specifications for double metal CMOS standard cells, both analog and digital, for a channeled system. Notice that power rails are at the same position and the P-wells also interconnect by abutment. The inputs and outputs are on a 15 micron grid and appear on both sides of the cell, that is, they are available at the routing channel on either side of the cell.

Cells are of constant height, namely 150 microns for a single supply and 220 microns for a dual supply rail. Although inputs and outputs can be spaced as close as 15 microns, this is not necessary. They must simply align with this grid. To make interconnection from the upper to the lower channel, dummy lines can run through any cell, or special dummy cells can be placed in between active cells to give interconnection between routing channels. For the cells given in Figure 4.1, the vertical runs into and through cells are in metal 2 while the horizontal routing in the channels is in metal 1. The horizontal power lines are also in metal 1. Figure 4.2 shows part of the routing of a channeled gate array.

4.3 Cell library

The usefulness of the standard cell concept depends very much upon the size and quality of the library. Most people offering a service will provide both data books and the cell information as part of their software. For digital work the size and complexity of cells can vary considerably. Most vendors have a comprehensive library of small logic and flip-flop cells called standard cells. Appendix 1 gives such a list. However, for many applications a far greater range of cells is needed. Some organizations classify their cells under various categories depending upon their size (in terms of transistor complexity). For example, terms like macro cells, mega modules, mega cells and supercells are used. In the largest categories the cells may be fixed or parameterized. For example, an 8-bit synchronous counter is an example of a fixed cell, where as an n-bit one, where n can be specified between 1 and 16, is a parameterized one. Parameterized cells can include counters, shift registers, programmable logic arrays, random access memories and read only memories. While microprocessors, in the form of bit slice machines, could be parameterized, it is more usual to hold in library specific microprocessor types such as a 6502, 6809 or Z80. Table 4.1 gives further examples of large library cells. As illustrated in Figure 4.3 the standard cell approach is to map onto silicon the required system using cells of different complexity from the library.

Table 4.1 Examples of super cells

Complete microprocessors (6502, Z80, 6809, etc.)
Bit slice microprocessors
Microprocessor peripherals (CRT controllers, PIAs, bus controller)
Parameterized counter/timer
Parameterized shift registers
Programmable logic arrays
Random access memories
Read only memories

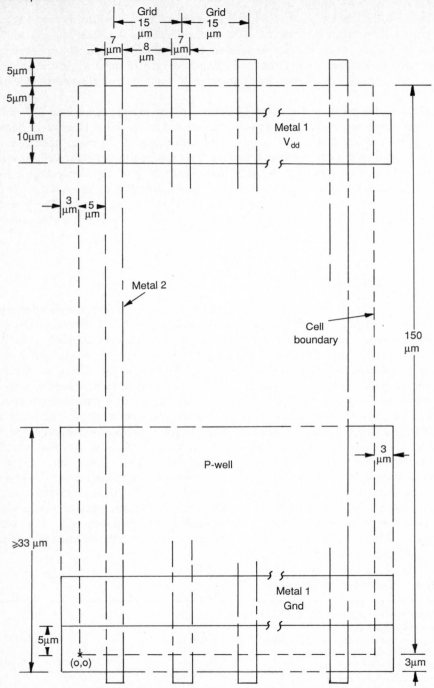

Figure 4.1   Typical P-well CMOS double metal standard cell specification for
(a) digital,

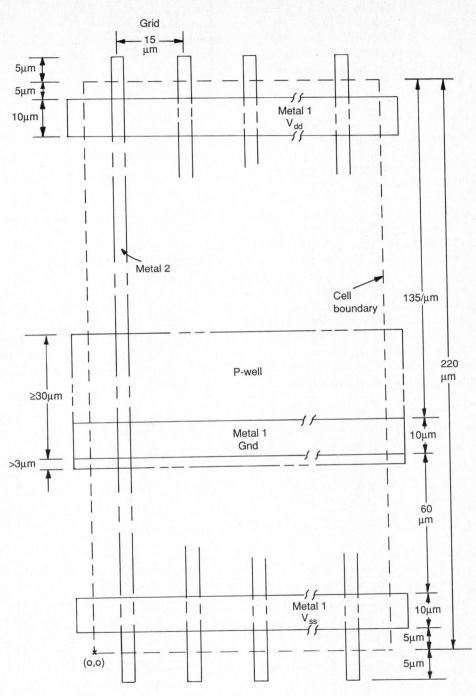

(b) analog cells

The information given on simple digital cells must include geometric information, giving cell length and grid positions of input and output points. Any feed-through lines should also be supplied. Technical specifications will include the logical operations, input and output capacities and information on speed. For simple CMOS gates it is usual to give this as a simple linear relationship, that is:

$$t_d = t_i + k C_L \tag{4.1}$$

where t_d is the circuit delay
  t_i is the intrinsic delay
  k is the scaling constant per unit load capacity
  C_L is the load capacity the circuit is driving

The constants t_i and k must be supplied for each circuit to calculate the delay time. Figure 4.4 shows a typical page from a standard cell data book.

In the case of analog circuits, standard cell libraries are usually not as well prepared. It is difficult to summarize the details. Figure 4.5 shows in pie chart form the type of analog circuits used in discrete circuit design.

The standard cell library should cover all these basic types including some of the industrial consumer types, for example solenoid/relay drivers. Appendix 1 provides a list of analog cells in one standard cell library.

The final cell types are the pads. These must be input and output, both for digital and analog signals. Various drive capabilities both on and off chip must be allowed for. Protection against electrostatic discharge (ESD) must also be built in. Appendix 1 lists pad types for a typical standard cell library.

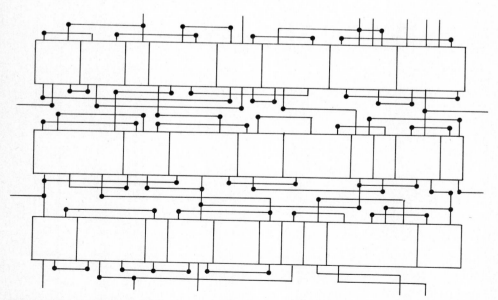

Figure 4.2   Routing for a channeled standard cell design

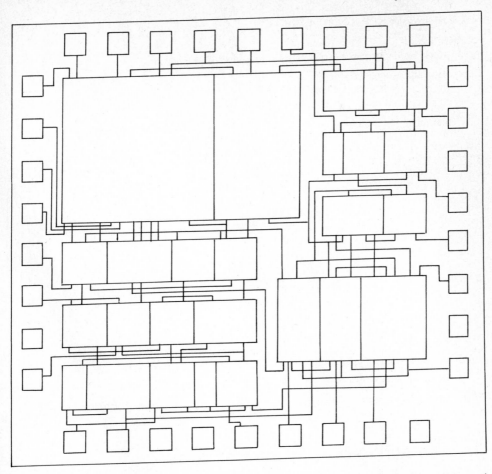

Figure 4.3 Illustrative example of a standard cell design using both standard and super cells

Two-input exclusive NOR   CPD3EXNOR/C/H

Cell description
A high speed two-input gate that performs the exclusive NOR function.

Dimensions are: Height 150 microns
                Width 105 microns

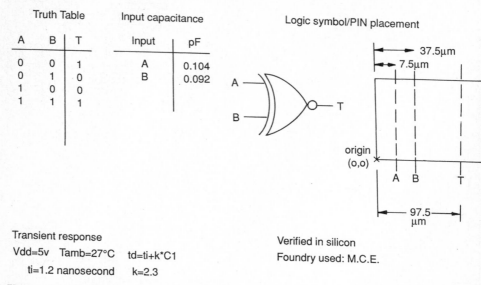

Truth Table

A	B	T
0	0	1
0	1	0
1	0	0
1	1	1

Input capacitance	
Input	pF
A	0.104
B	0.092

Logic symbol/PIN placement

Transient response
Vdd=5v Tamb=27°C   td=ti+k*C1
    ti=1.2 nanosecond   k=2.3

Verified in silicon
Foundry used: M.C.E.

Figure 4.4   Example of a 3 micron P-well CMOS double metal standard cell

4.4   Selecting a standard cell vendor

The criteria for selecting a standard cell vendor is basically the same as for the gate array case (section 3.4), that is:

1. service offered
2. technical specifications
3. cost
4. second sourcing.

Perhaps three factors that require further discussion are:

1. library size
2. up-front costs
3. workstations required.

As stated previously, the library size and what it contains is important. It will significantly influence how much is placed on a chip and how much off a chip. Simple gate libraries infer that the standard cell chip being designed is small and perhaps similar in function to that which is achieved through a gate array. However, if there are parameterized cells, microprocessor and a full range of analog cells, complete sophisticated systems can be placed on the integrated circuit.

Because there is little sharing of processing costs, the up-front costs are likely to be high. Even if for prototypes a wafer is shared with other customers, there could be additional mask-making charges when ready to go to full production volumes. In fact, the initial cost-sharing benefits may prove to be false. The whole thrust of integrated circuit design is towards correct design the first time and, if that is true, then it is preferable to go direct to production masks at the start.

The question of workstation depends on how much design is to be undertaken in-house. Because standard cell designs can be very complex, a simple workstation can cause frustrations for a designer waiting for the machines to complete simulation runs. On the other hand, as seen in Chapter 1, the cost of a good workstation can be high. Some vendors only offer standard cell software that will run on an expensive workstation, while others also assume that you have certain software packages from the workstation's suppliers. One thing is certain. If a vendor recommends a particular workstation (and it is what they themselves use) then it is preferable to use the same. Although expensive, it will speed up design time, allow greater interaction with the vendor and could even reduce costs in the long term. By way of example we wasted fifteen months trying to solve problems associated with a vendor's software to get it running correctly on an alternative cheaper workstation.

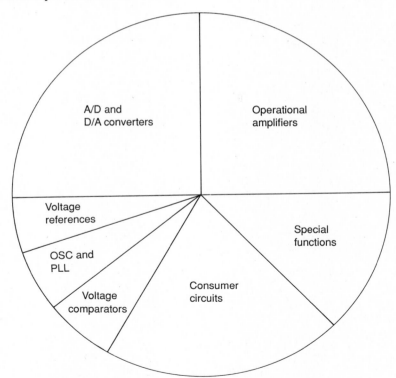

Figure 4.5   Types of discrete analog circuits employed in designs

4.5 Questions

1.   Define the following terms:
     (a) standard cell
     (b) macro cell
     (c) standard cell library.
2. What advantages does the standard cell approach offer over gate arrays?
3. Table 4.1 provides several examples of super cells. Can you suggest other classes that would be useful to have in a library?
4. Figure 4.6 graphs the actual delay times for a CMOS cell. Does equation 4.1 provide a good model for this circuit? Calculate appropriate constants for the model.

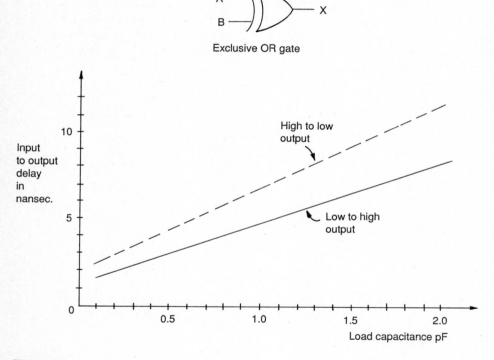

Figure 4.6

4.6 Selected vendors' literature

AMI (1982). 'Designing with gate arrays—a training course (3 parts)', American Microsystems Inc., California, USA (published as an insert in *Electronic Engineering*, vol. 54, March to May, 1982).

GE/RCA (1987). *Solid State Data Book, ASIC SC-3000, 1.5 micron standard cell library*, Somerville, USA.

Micro Circuit Engineering (1985). *Fulmar Service*, Tewkesbury, UK.

Motorola (1986). *2 micron Standard Cell Data Book*, ASIC Division, Arizona, USA.

NCR Corporation (1987). *ASIC Data Book, Standard Cell and Gate Array Libraries*, Ohio, USA.

VLSI Technology Incorporated (1987). *VMC Series—Advanced 2 micron CMOS Megacell Family*, California, USA.

4.7 Selected standard cell suppliers

AMCC
Fujitsu
GE/RCA/AWA
Gould/AMI
Harris
Hitachi
International Micro Products
Intel
LSI Logic
Micro Circuit Engineering
Motorola
National/Fairchild

NCR
NEC
Plessey/Ferranti
Philips/Signetics
Siemens
Silicon Systems
Texas Instruments
Thomson/SGS
Toshiba
VLSI Technology
Zymos

5   Full custom and silicon compilers

5.1   Introduction

By full custom it is meant that a chip is designed from scratch to meet a particular need. Library cells may or may not be used. The emphasis is on achieving the ultimate in electrical performance and minimum silicon area. It is the approach that is taken for chips having very large production runs as it gives the best performance at minimum cost (Figure 1.7). The penalty is that there is a large time factor and a large up-front cost for there is little or no sharing of costs. Depending on the chip size and complexity, some 5 to 10 person years of effort may be required for each chip design.

Silicon compilers satisfy those cases where only a few samples are required of specialized complex chips. A silicon compiler accepts a description of the system (usually in textual form) and produces mask and test information for the silicon chip. Present silicon compilers are not silicon-area efficient, but they are fast so that a design may be completed by a single person in one or two weeks. Thus the design costs are minimized, but the fabrication costs are usually higher. For small volume runs the net saving could be significant.

5.2   Full custom design

Since the beginning of integrated circuits, this has been the normal method of design. The method requires specialist people who have detailed circuit, silicon process and computing skills. While this was adequate for the design of small standard function integrated circuits, with the rapid growth in chip complexity whole systems can be placed on a chip, so that the chip designer is now forced to work with a system designer.

The Mead and Conway (1980) approach opened up the way for digital system designers to undertake their own full custom design. By 1987 (Haskard & May) texts were appearing showing how analog circuits could also be added by system designers to their own chips. Generally, there is a cost penalty for this approach, as system designers cannot achieve the same circuit performance as skilled chip designers.

The approach employed is to try and minimize the area needed for routing of signals. We saw in Section 4.1 that for gate arrays as much as 75 percent of the area is used for routing. With full custom the desire is to reduce the routing area to less than 25 percent, that is, a reversal of figures for the gate array, making at least 75 percent of the full custom silicon area available for active circuits.

To achieve a good full custom design, three principles must be employed:

1. a floor plan driven approach;
2. a hierarchical design; and
3. designing for testability.

We will consider each of these in turn.

5.2.1   Floor plans

The concept is similar to that an architect employs to design a building. The room requirements, expressed in areas, are juggled and fitted together as a floor plan until the best solution is determined. A chip floor plan is the way in which the functional modules that make up the system are best mapped onto the silicon. Thus, a floor plan driven design is where the chip floor plan is the *current solution* as to how the functional modules, expressed in physical form, are best mapped onto the silicon. It is an evolutionary process allowing:

1. study of alternative architectures;
2. optimization of global communications; and
3. control of the chip–aspect ratio.

Each of these three aspects is vital for the successful completion of a full custom chip.

The selection of the correct algorithm is important in achieving the speed requirements and a satisfactory layout. The floor plan approach, being a top-down design approach, allows various architectures to be compared. The best algorithms are frequently those that allow considerable replication, that is, a basic building block repeated many times.

By placing function blocks in the correct location, global communications can be minimized. With the alternative bottom up design approach, one concentrates on communications at the gate level. Saving a few square microns here may create global problems requiring much larger areas of silicon to solve them.

Today most full custom designs are for large chips and therefore the chip–aspect ratio is important, for the chip must eventually be packaged. Most packages are designed to accept square chips, so that ideally the chip–aspect ratio should be kept in the range of 0.8 to 1.2. Should this not be the case, then a larger more expensive package may have to be employed.

The usual method of carrying out a floor plan driven approach is to commence with a floor plan based on the system block diagram. Placement of the blocks is modified to allow input/outputs to the pads at the periphery and to minimize communication problems. Next the block sizes are estimated—some may even need to be designed if no suitable one is available from a library—and appropriate adjustments made to the floor plan. Wire details are added for power, clocks, signals, etc. Which metal layers are used is also specified. Propagation delays may need to be checked and a further rearrangement of the floor plan made. It is an iterative process. As more detailed information on the individual blocks is determined, so the floor plan is adjusted. Similarly, floor plan constraints are fed down to adjust the block–aspect ratios and positions of signal input and outputs. This is all illustrated in Figure 5.1.

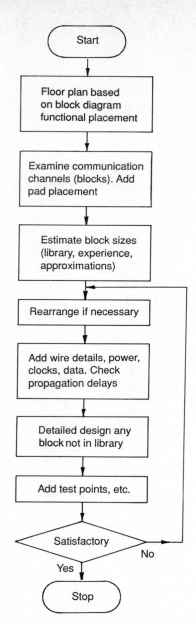

Figure 5.1   Flow diagram of a floor plan driven approach

5.2.2   Hierarchical design

It should be remembered that the communication channels are also considered as function blocks and it is the intention to minimize their size. Thus, the cell's design should make interconnection by abutment.

5.2.3 Designing for testability

Because many full custom chips are large and complex, the problem of testing them is also complex. While voltage contrast methods using a scanning electron microscope or laser writing methods can be employed to set internal states of the chip, on-chip testing is a more usual approach. Here, additional circuitry/pads are added to the chip to enable it to be tested.

How the final chip is to be tested is a question that must be considered at the commencement of the design. If the chip consists simply of combinational logic, then the testing time to test all combinations grows linearly with the number of gates. If the number of gates in a signal path increases (an increase in logical depth), then the testing time grows exponentially with logical depth. Should the chip also contain memory elements, that is, an increase in sequential depth, then there are initialization problems. The inclusion of testing procedures in the design stage is called structured design.

To enable testing to occur a chip should have:

1. good controlability, that is, the ability to control a network within an integrated circuit under test;
2. good observability, or the ability to observe a network within an integrated circuit; and
3. good predictability, which is a measure of the controlability to initialize sequential circuits.

Various software programs such as COMET and SCOAP (Hess, 1982) allow logic architectures to be examined and compared for controlability and observability. Methods employed in the design to enable built-in testing of a chip include:

1. *Partitioning*, where the system is broken down into several such units, often the combinational logic circuits being separated from the sequential circuits;
2. *Bus methods*, where the chip is organized as a bus structure where multiplexers switch in blocks for testing; gradually, the total system can be built up (Figure 5.3).
3. *Scan path methods*, where either the memory elements of the chip are connected into a shift register snake, to preset memory elements and read their contents (IBM, Level Sensitive Scan Design method; see Figure 5.4) or a separate snake shift register is built in to achieve the same result (Scan/Set method).
4. *Signature analysis*, an adaptation of a method devised by Hewlett Packard, is where half the memory elements are connected as a pseudo random pattern generator used to generate input signals, and the remaining memory elements employed as a signature register to monitor the output. The pattern generator and signature register (Figure 5.5) are both fed from the same clock for a set number of cycles. The resultant number in the signature register indicates whether the chip is good or not. To cover the case of the signature register stuck at the correct signature number, the memory elements in the pattern generator and signature register are often reversed and a second test undertaken.

Which of these methods is used depends on the system being integrated and what the designer believes to be a reasonable amount of additional circuit complexity to be added to the chip to simplify testing. At most the area increase should be 25 percent with 15 to 20 percent considered more desirable.

5.3   Silicon compilation (Gajski, 1985)

The first silicon compilers were based on programmable logic generators (Ayres, 1983). Since all combinational logic functions can be expressed in the canonical minterm form, one can generate a parameterised cell to perform any combinational logic function. Figure 5.6 illustrates this.

The generator can be extended to produce a finite state machine, where the programmable logic generator performs the combinational logic and the delay or memory elements are achieved through clocking the inputs of the input and output inverters (Figure 5.7). Programs such as PLAGEN are simple silicon compilers, where the specification is fed in, in textual form, and the output is either a simple combinational logic circuit or a finite state machine.

Today there is a range of silicon compiler programs. Examples include Bristle Blocks (Johannsen, 1979), MacPitts (Fox, 1983) and First (Denyer et al., 1982). Unfortunately, there is no general purpose silicon compiler. That is, the compilers that have been written are all for specific systems, typically digital filters or a microprocessor system. The software accepts a specification in textual form, works out the function blocks needed, decides on an appropriate floor plan and places the blocks accordingly. The output is mask information to make a chip to perform the required function. At present they are wasteful on silicon area, but are extremely useful when only a few sample quantities of a complex system are needed quickly.

To assist in the development of new silicon compilers, special languages and programs have been written to allow people to generate their own compilers. GDT and Genesis are two such generation tools (Evanczuk, 1985). Other companies make use of simple silicon compilers to generate simple cells to build up their standard cell libraries. Overall, because compilers are still not silicon-area efficient they are mainly restricted to use in educational and research establishments.

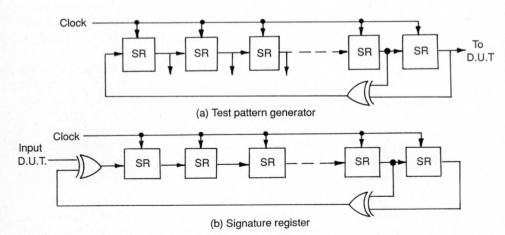

(a) Test pattern generator

(b) Signature register

Figure 5.5   Construction of memory elements as shift registers to form a pattern generator and signature register for signature analysis

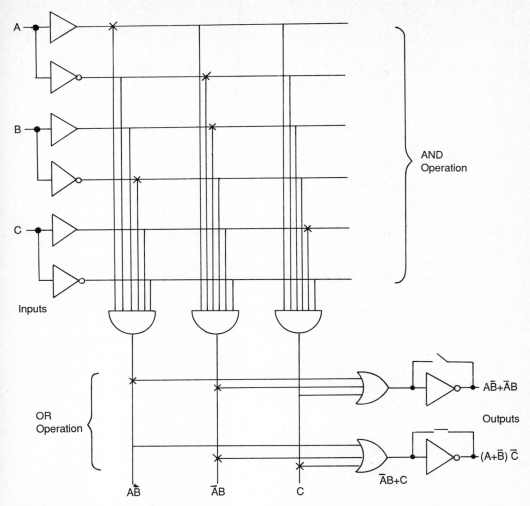

Figure 5.6 Example of a simple compiler based on a programmable logic generator

5.4 Questions

1. Two important aspects of full custom design are:
   (a) a floor plan driven approach;
   (b) built-in testability.
   Discuss why they are so important.
2. Consider the block diagram of a sample data system given in Figure 5.8. The system has eight blocks performing various functions and by each is given the best estimate of the silicon area that it will occupy. The timing generator and control unit generate

signals that must be routed to the other blocks. For example 2T indicates that there are two timing signals to be routed. The central bus is 8-bit parallel.

The system requires 17 pads as follows:

No. of pads	Function	Pad size (microns)
8	Bi-directional bus	250 × 500
1	Analog input	250 × 200
1	System reset	250 × 200
3	Control inputs	250 × 200
2	Crystal oscillator	250 × 250
2	Supply rails	250 × 150

Note: The distance between the centre line of pads must be at least 250 microns.

Figure 5.1 suggests that the first floor plan can be based on a system block diagram. Devise an initial floor plan for the sample data system.

3. Explain the principle of the Scan Path method of testing. Implementation can take two forms. In the LSSD system all memory elements are connected into a long shift register in the test mode, whereas with the Scan/Set approach a separate shift resister is built into the chip to move information in and out. Compare the two methods, listing what you see are the advantages and disadvantages of each method.

4. Early silicon compilers used for generating combinational logic layouts employed as the basic element an expandable NOR gate. Thus to achieve the AND operation De Morgan's theorem was invoked and the complement signals employed. Figure 5.9 shows how the extendable NOR gate was mapped out onto the silicon. Investigate how this concept can be expanded to make the simple programmable logic array given in Figure 5.6. (*Hint*: First convert the schematic to NOR gates and inverters and then map onto silicon.)

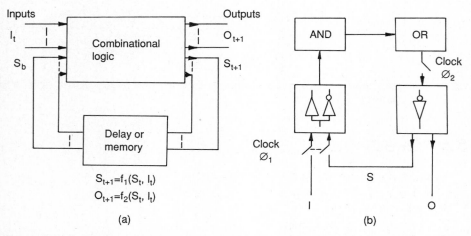

Figure 5.7 Finite state machine: (a) concept, and (b) realization through a modified programmable logic generator. Φ_1 and Φ_2 are a two-phase non-overlapping clock

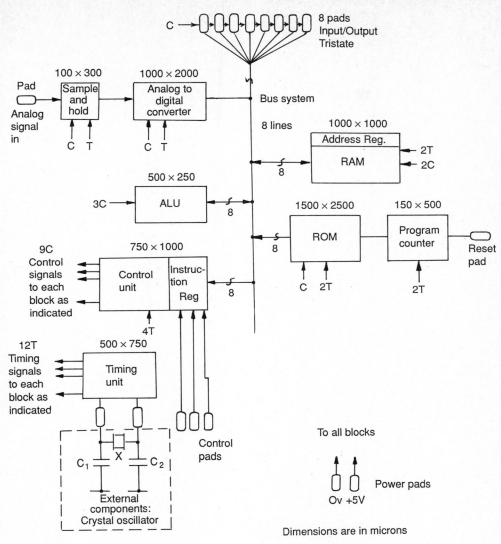

Figure 5.8

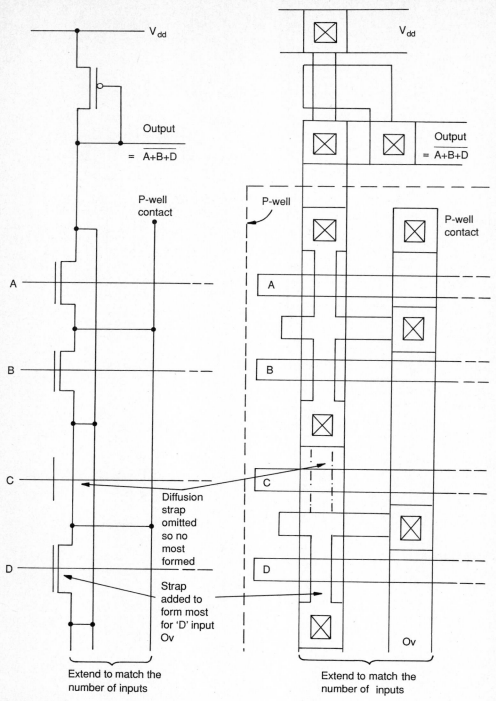

V_{dd}

Output

= $\overline{A+B+D}$

P-well
contact

A

B

C

Diffusion
strap
omitted
so no
most
formed

D

Strap
added to
form most
for 'D' input
Ov

Extend to match the
number of inputs

V_{dd}

Output

= $\overline{A+B+D}$

P-well

P-well
contact

A

B

C

D

Ov

Extend to match the
number of inputs

Figure   5.9

5.5 Bibliography

Ayres, R. F. (1983). *VLSI Silicon Compilation and the Art of Automatic Microchip Design*, Prentice Hall, New York.

Denyer, P. B., Renshaw, D. & Bergmann, N. (1982). 'A silicon compiler for VLSI signal processors', *ESSCIRC'82, Digest of Technical Papers*, Brussels, September, p.215–18.

Evanczuk, S. (1985). 'Silicon compilers: No automatic route to acceptance',*VLSI Systems Design*, vol. 6, November, p.42–4.

Fox, J. R. (1983). 'The MacPitts silicon compiler: A view from the telecommunications industry', *VLSI Design*, vol. 4, May/June, p.30–7.

Gajski, D. D. (1985). 'Silicon compilation', *VLSI Systems Design*, vol. 6, November, p.48–64.

Haskard, M. R. & May, I. C. (1987). *Analog VLSI Design; nMOS and CMOS*, Prentice Hall, New York.

Hess, R. D. (1982). 'Testability analysis: An alternative to structured design for testability', *VLSI Design*, vol. 3, March/April, p.22–9.

Johannsen, D. (1979). 'Bristle blocks: A silicon compiler', 16th Design Automation Conference, San Diego, California, USA.

Mead, C. & Conway, L. (1980). *Introduction to VLSI Systems*, Addison-Wesley, Reading, UK.

6 Software

6.1 Introduction

The design of integrated circuits has probably led the field in computer-aided design (CAD). There are several reasons for this. The design is basically the production of several two-dimensional drawings, each drawing representing a mask used in the fabrication process. This is something that can be readily done with a computer. Figure 6.1 shows a designer laying out a gate array chip using a workstation employing a mouse to move the cursor.

The design process also involves the simulation of circuits and systems. With the rapid increase in chip complexity it is no longer possible to breadboard an integrated circuit to test it, for not only are there just too many transistors, but the parasitic

Figure 6.1   A typical workstation used for the design of integrated circuits

reactances and resistances of a breadboard system differ considerably from those on chip. Thus, at best, a breadboard system can only test correctness of static function. Timing, race conditions, glitch generation and analog circuit stability cannot be verified on a breadboard system. The solution to this problem is to employ computer simulation methods.

Perhaps a final reason for using CAD methods is the speeding up of designers' output. Figure 6.2 shows the experiences of the Microelectronics Centre.

6.2 Software requirements

The introductory section suggests that the use of CAD performs two major roles:

1. integrated circuit layout and parameter extraction; and
2. simulation and test vector generation.

These will be considered in turn.

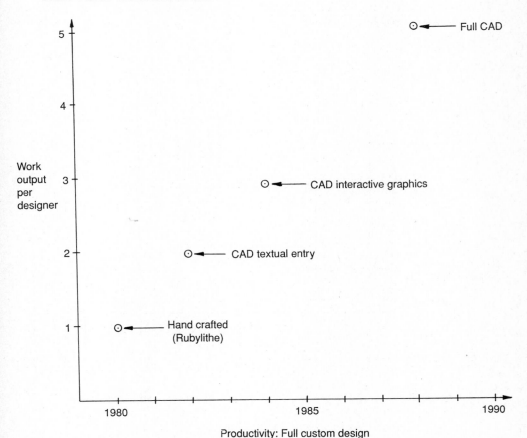

Figure 6.2 Increase in productivity of a design engineer through the introduction of computer-aided design methods

6.2.1   Layout and extraction software

The purpose of this software is to produce the artwork for each mask layer in the process and provide an interface with the simulation software. The software must also check all line widths and spacings to ensure that no foundry layout rule has been violated. Manually this would be a tedious process and prone to error. All the foundry-process information is placed in a technology file, a separate file is required for each foundry process.

Over the years various levels of software have been produced, starting from simple textual input through to silicon compilation. These will briefly be considered in turn.

1. *Textual entry*

This is the most primitive software and is one level up from the manual method. Normally the designer undertakes a trial layout on graph paper, digitises it and feeds it into the computer via the keyboard. Accurate plots at a specified scale are produced for checking. A technology file containing all minimum layout criteria allows a design rule checking program to verify, at the end, that no geometric errors have occurred. In most cases there is no parameter or circuit extraction. Figure 6.3 is an example of a textual input program.

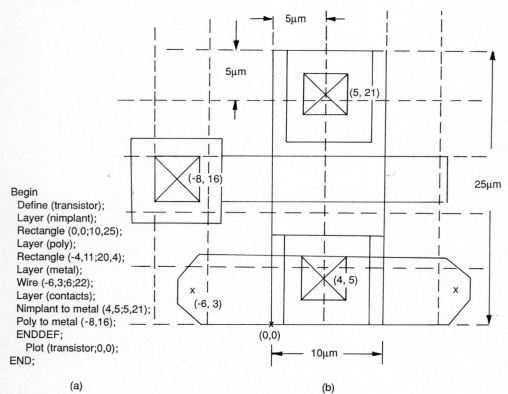

```
Begin
  Define (transistor);
  Layer (nimplant);
  Rectangle (0,0;10,25);
  Layer (poly);
  Rectangle (-4,11;20,4);
  Layer (metal);
  Wire (-6,3;6,22);
  Layer (contacts);
  Nimplant to metal (4,5;5,21);
  Poly to metal (-8,16);
  ENDDEF;
    Plot (transistor;0,0);
END;
```

(a)   (b)

Figure 6.3 Example of textual input software; (a) written in PASCAL, (b) the resultant transistor

2. *Interactive entry*

Here the designer is able to interact with the computer using it as a drafting board. Input is normally via a menu with responses made using the keyboard and a mouse. As with the textual input software, the designer is still concerned about layers, boxes and wires, or those primitives that must be combined to make discrete devices. Design rule checking occurs either in a batch mode at the conclusion of a design, or as the primitives are drawn. Both analog and digital chips can be designed in this way.

Circuit extraction software may also occur at this level. Once the section of a design is completed, the program, on command, extracts and displays the final circuit as a circuit diagram, with important parasitic elements. This allows the designer to see that no errors have been made and that the dominant parasitic components are acceptable. The program may also provide a file of the correct format for feeding into simulation programs.

3. *Symbolic entry*

Such programs are concerned with systems at the circuit level. The designer interactively specifies on the screen the transistors and interconnections needed for the circuit. The program assigns standard dimensions to the transistors and lays out the geometry, compacting the layout to the minimum allowable size. The technology file in the program requires more information than the interactive entry software packages. These software packages are normally menu driven and at present are only suitable for digital systems.

Parameter extraction occurs and the extracted information is placed in a format ready for the simulation program.

4. *Schematic entry*

Using an interactive input to a workstation, the schematic diagram for the system is entered. Only cells that are in the software library can be used. The technology file is again more complex than the previous software listed. Not only does it contain geometric and device details, but also details on each library cell.

Routing of the cells is normally automatic and once completed, wiring parasitic elements are extracted ready for simulation. A net list is often produced.

Depending on the extent of the cell library this class of software may allow analog circuits as well as digital.

Figure 6.4 gives an example of a menu driven schematic entry software package, while Appendix 3 provides details on a low cost schematic entry CAD package that allows both gate array and standard cell designs.

5. *Silicon compilation*

This is the most sophisticated form of entry. It completes the loop in that entry is normally back to textual; a textual description of the system in a high level language and the output is mask information for the chip. At present, the software is very restrictive in the type of system that can be designed. Section 5.3 discusses this type of software in more detail.

In listing the software types, it should be noted that the interactive entry is probably the most flexible in that it gives the designer the greatest freedom and allows both analog and digital circuits to be designed. Normally the cell libraries used in the schematic entry software are designed by skilled integrated circuit designers, using the interactive method of entry.

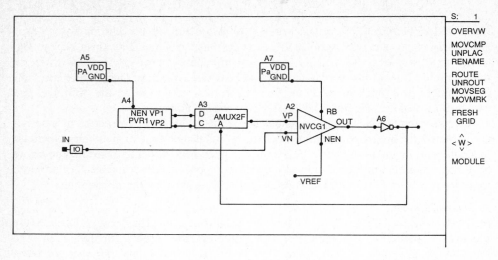

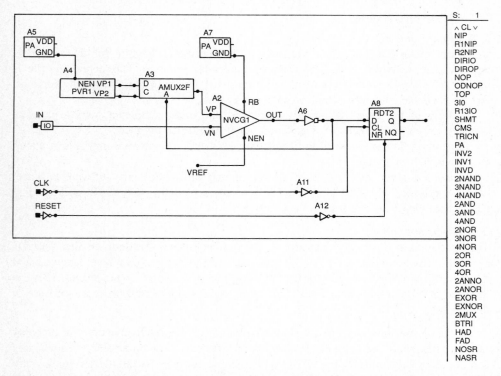

Figure 6.4   Schematic entry software from a simple IBM clone computer screen showing two different menus (*Micro Circuit Engineering*)

6.2.2 Simulation and test vector software

For a full and complete simulation of a circuit, an analog simulation program, such as SPICE, is normally required. Unfortunately, the computing time taken can be excessively long and a compromise is often required between accuracy and computer run time. For digital systems, a switch level simulator is the preferred method. They come in various degrees of sophistication expressed by the numbers of levels. Thus a 6-level switch simulator will show '0' states, '1' states, rising edges, falling edges, don't care states and glitches. Output from the simulators are normally timing waveforms displayed on the workstations.

The simulation of an integrated circuit is often a mixture of analog and switch level simulation. For example, in schematic entry the cells in the library have usually undergone extensive analog simulation to verify their performance under all possible conditions. The full simulation of the schematic entered would be undertaken in a switch level mode, the program making use of the more detailed information from the analog simulation of each cell.

For analog systems there is little choice—analog simulation programs must be used. Thus a system employing a mixture of analog and digital circuits is more difficult to simulate. First, the analog portion must be simulated using an analog simulation program, followed by the digital portion often using a switch mode simulator.

Most of the recent layout programs perform parameter extraction and assemble them in the required format for entry into the simulation program. The translation of the extracted geometric data into electrical data calls for additional details to be held in a technology file. Factors such as capacity per unit area, sheet resistance for layers and transistor parameters must be included. Again analog circuits are more difficult than digital for a greater degree of precision is needed in extracting parameters. Not only are there a larger number of critical parasitics, but their values must be determined accurately to ensure correct simulation.

With the simulation completed and the designer having confirmed that the chip will work, the simulated data is used to generate a set of test vectors. Thus when the chips are fabricated there is a set of test information that allows speedy checking of the integrated circuits. It is normal to arrange for the test vector information to be of the correct format to be fed into the foundry's testing machine.

6.3 Interfacing with a vendor

The software previously discussed can be split into two types: that which concentrates on device design and that which looks at system design. Using the latter type, it is not necessary for a product manufacturer to be skilled in integrated circuit design. Consider Figure 6.5 which shows the design stages that must be undertaken for an application specific integrated circuit (ASIC).

The product idea must first be translated into a specification from which a detailed schematic diagram is generated. To verify that this is correct, a functional simulation test is undertaken. Any errors can be corrected at this point. Once the schematic diagram is correct, both net and test vector lists can be produced using the computer workstation. The next stage is to lay out the integrated circuit using one of the software package types described in the previous section. When this has been completed, parasitics must be extracted and the simulation program re-run to verify that the chip will meet both the functional and timing requirements. If any design errors show up in the simulation run, then corrections must be made. The design, when correct, is then forwarded to the foundry for mask making and fabrication.

When fabrication is completed by the foundry, the chips, still in wafer form, are static-probe tested to ensure defective devices are rejected. After sawing and breaking the wafer into dice, the good dice are packaged. They then undergo detailed testing using the test vectors generated during the design phase.

As seen from Figure 6.5, there are three points where the design can be interfaced with the vendor. The product manufacturer's design team can undertake the complete design and simply transfer the mask data to a foundry for processing. Even the final

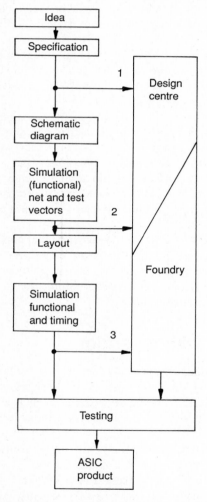

Figure 6.5   The ASIC design and manufacturing process

acceptance testing can be shared between the manufacturer and the foundry. In this case the design team must have full knowledge of the foundry process and adequate integrated circuit design skills. If the ASIC does not operate correctly, then it is the product manufacturer's error. The transfer of information is achieved via a magnetic tape, cassette or floppy disk using an agreed format such as GDS-2, CIF or ELECTROMASK.

The second interface point is after a correct schematic diagram has been produced by the product manufacturer. The design exercise up to this point, requires little knowledge of silicon (or gallium arsenide) processing. The schematic diagram simply uses standard

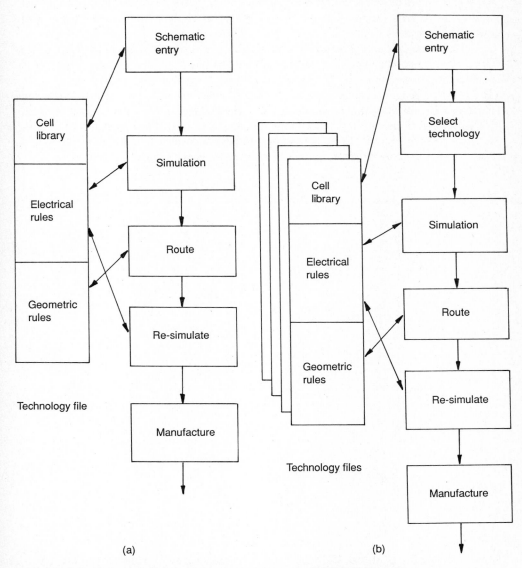

(a)   (b)

Figure 6.6 The essential steps and components of ASIC CAD software functions available from the vendor's library. There is a further advantage in interfacing at this point, in that it allows the product manufacturer full control of the system design and the vendor/foundry full control of the integrated circuit design and manufacture. The exchange media is either a cartridge or floppy disk, the format details set by the vendor's software.

The third and final point of interfacing is to bring in a design team once the specification has been documented. The design team, either from a separate design house or the foundry's, undertake the design from hereon. Many product manufacturers believe that this is an unacceptable point of interfacing, as they must disclose too much on their new products and design strategy. However, for others it is seen as the point that minimizes their risks.

Of the three points of interfacing with a vendor, the middle route (2 on Figure 6.5) appears to be a good compromise and therefore is the one that is most commonly used. A manufacturer changing to ASICs for the first time may choose to go via the earlier route (1) until confidence is gained, while experienced manufacturers may reduce costs and maintain full control by taking route 3. In all instances it is stressed that a good working relationship with the selected vendor/foundry should be established right from the start. No matter which route is taken, if both parties have a correct understanding of what is required from the very outset, there will be reduced costs and errors.

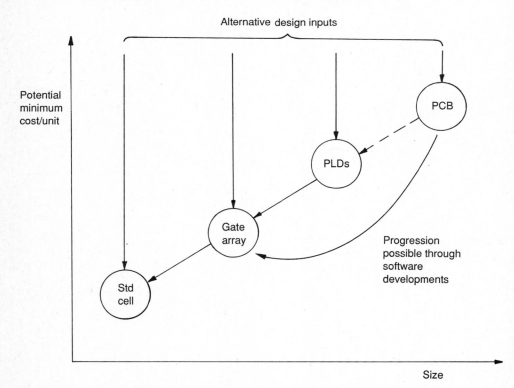

Figure 6.7 Ability of some ASIC CAD software packages to allow a flow from one technology to another

6.4 Software extensions

The design process discussed in the previous section can be expanded as shown in Figure 6.6(a). For schematic entry there must be access to a library of cells. To simulate the system there must be a set of electrical parameters and rules, while the mapping of the circuit onto silicon requires detailed geometric or layout rules. All of this additional information is held in a library and technology file. Often the designer is unaware of all this detailed information as the CAD software simply prompts the designer, makes corrections when minor errors are made or undertakes the process, such as routing, automatically.

In order to make the design software more flexible, some software houses include a whole range of technology files as shown in Figure 6.6(b). For example, the Micro Circuit Engineering software (Appendix 3) supplies both 5 and 3 micron gate array process information and the designer selects the technology that provides the best performance–cost relationship for the product. Some software even includes technology and library files for different foundries so that the designer now has the choice of interfacing with one of a number of foundries to achieve better second sourcing. In the case of the BX software, this is also possible. A common library is used and Micro Circuit Engineering acts as the silicon broker.

Recently software writers have started to exploit the fact that the modules in an ASIC CAD package are basically the same no matter which type of ASIC is being designed. These are the modules on the right-hand side of the two flow diagrams given in Figure 6.6. They are the schematic entry, simulation, routing and manufacturing interface software. Consequently, if the CAD package is correctly assembled, the technology files need not be restricted to a single ASIC type. Already some printed circuit board and programmable logic device software packages allow gate array options, while the Micro Circuit Engineering BX software allows both gate array and standard cell designs. This capability allows the product manufacturer to optimize product costs by starting with one technology and changing to another as sales volumes increase (Figure 1.7). Figure 6.7 illustrates this software extension concept.

6.5 Questions

1. By increasing the degree of CAD sophistication from interactive to symbolic to schematic through to silicon compilation textual entry, greater constraints are often placed on the designer. Thus there is a trade off of universal application and flexibility of the software against speeding up the design process and correctness of a first time design. Is this a good thing? Discuss the case for a totally digital system and then for one that has a mixture of analog and digital circuits.
2. There are four essential steps when designing a silicon integrated circuit:
   (a) Propose a schematic diagram.
   (b) Test the schematic diagram through simulation.
   (c) Map out the circuit onto silicon.
   (d) Extract the parasitics and re-simulate to confirm correct operation.

nformation is needed by the software to undertake the last three steps
tically? At this stage why cannot step (a) be readily undertaken automatically?
ing with a vendor/foundry at the schematic entry interface (point 2 on Figure
ɔften seen as the most efficient and cost effective entry point. Discuss this
statement.

7 Programmable logic devices

7.1 Introduction

Many small manufacturers believe that the risks in changing to ASIC technology are still too great. The investment in the non-return engineering costs commit them to a particular path, the use of ASIC prevents the firm making last minute design changes and, finally, employing vendors to design the ASICs requires them to reveal their design concepts and ideas to other parties. While there is some truth in each of these statements, good management practices can reduce these risks to a point where they are of little consequence.

For small organizations, the programmable logic devices (PLDs) are a viable alternative. They are standard products that can be programmed in-house to a manufacturer's requirement. Even large organizations are turning to them for prototyping a system. Their advantages (Agrowal & Laws, 1984) include:

1. fast programming of devices;
2. no non-return engineering charges;
3. low equipment costs to design and program;
4. immediate in-circuit checking;
5. if a reprogrammable PLD is employed, then any errors can be corrected with the device not wasted.

While new types of PLDs appear daily, they still have several disadvantages. First, their size is currently limited to less than 10 000 equivalent gates. Most types are less than 2000 gates. More importantly, because they are not as flexible as gate arrays, standard cell or full custom, a large range of different product types is required, each vendor producing its own solution and product range. Of late, there have been agreements between foundries to second source each other, but there can be traps. Two products with the same type number from different foundries can require different waveforms to program them (DATA I/O Corp., 1986). Finally, larger devices can be expensive, costing several hundred dollars per chip.

7.2 The history of programmable logic devices

In the early 1970s programmable read only memories (PROM) based on fusable link technology appeared. They were frequently used for changing the micro code in micro controlled microprocessors. Problems arose with aluminum fuses, the metal used for normal integrated circuit metalization, as the vaporized aluminum might do damage when it condenses on the integrated circuit surface. Very quickly nichrome became the preferred fuse material, being deposited by thin film vacuum technology and made several hundred angstrom units thick. The PROM structure was not unlike that of the programmable logic array (PLA) discussed in section 5.3, except that the AND gate array was fixed and the OR gate was programmable. This is shown in Figure 7.1(a).

In 1975, Signetic Corporation (Signetics, 1976) saw an extension of this technology, in that the PLA was a general purpose logic array. They developed fusible field programmable logic arrays (FPLA) where both the AND and OR gates of the PLAs were programmable. This is shown in Figure 7.1(c). Monolithic Memories on the other hand saw value in producing a PLA with a programmable AND gate array and fixed OR gate array. These devices were first marketed in the late 1970s and called Programmable Array Logic (PAL). They are also shown diagramatically in Figure 7.1(b).

These early PLDs, based on metal fusible link technology, were all bipolar devices. More recently other technologies have been introduced. These include:

1. polysilicon fuse technology;
2. antifuse technology, where the 'blowing' creates a short rather than an open circuit;
3. erasable CMOS devices based on both ultraviolet erasable and electrically erasable methods employed in ROMs; and
4. dynamic matrix switching methods called logic cell arrays (LCA).

The reprogrammable types are ideal for prototyping, as they can be readily modified many times. Once they are correct, cheaper equivalent fusible types can be employed in production.

At present there is about equal use of bipolar and CMOS types, but by later this decade it is expected that there will be over twice as many CMOS types used as bipolar (Hinder & Rappaport, 1987). The CMOS versions will have delays between input and output as low as 20 nanoseconds. Where higher speeds are required, TTL types will achieve speed down to 12 nanoseconds and ECL types 5 nanoseconds (Cole, 1987).

The internal structure of the PLDs has changed over the years (Elektor, 1985). Table 7.1 shows the major categories. The inclusion of registers allows memory functions, while internal feedback provides the capability for sequential circuits and state machines.

Table 7.1   Selection of classes of programmable gate arrays

Class 1	AND (fixed)	OR (variable)
	AND (variable)	OR (fixed)
	AND (variable)	OR (variable)
Class 2	AND OR	INVERT/NOT INVERT
	AND OR	INVERT/NOT INVERT WITH FEEDBACK
Class 3	AND OR	REGISTER
	AND OR	REGISTER WITH FEEDBACK
Class 4	AND OR	OTHER LOGIC (eg EX OR) REGISTER
	AND OR	OTHER LOGIC REGISTER WITH FEEDBACK

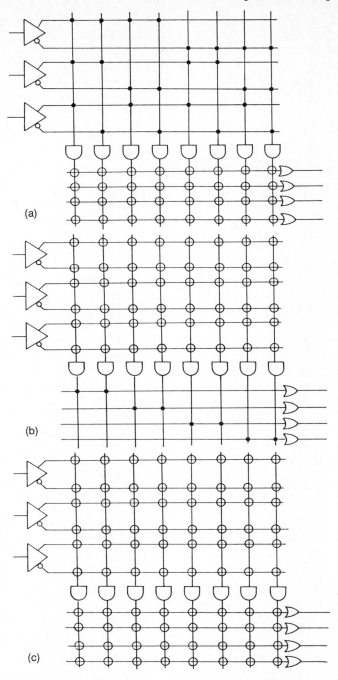

Figure 7.1 Development of programmable logic devices: (a) programmable read only memory (PROM) (b) programmable array logic (PAL) (c) field programmable logic array (FPLA)

One problem with PLDs is the range of names that different manufacturers have coined for their products. In addition to those already discussed—PLA, PAL, FPGA—they include programmable gate arrays (PGA), erasable programmable logic devices (EPLD), programmable logic sequencer (PLC), field programmable address decoder (FPAD) and multiple array matrix (MAX). Some of these latter devices are considered to be very application oriented and therefore there is a growing tendency to call programmable logic devices ASICs. This remains a debatable point, however, what is certain is that PLDs are starting to compete directly with small gate array products.

7.3 Programmable logic arrays

The basic structure of a programmable logic array is shown in Figure 7.2. It consists of input drivers, AND and OR arrays, and a configurable output block. The latter is programmed to allow active high or low or tristate output, inclusion of a flip-flop (one of several types as a rule) and whether or not there is feedback to the input AND array.

As can be seen, PLDs can be complex and, depending on the size of the two arrays and the amount of programming required, packages of up to 84 pins can be needed. To give greater flexibility and reduce pin count, some PLDs can have configurable pins, so that they can be programmed as either output or input. Thus a PLA may have a dedicated number of input and output pins with others programmable depending upon the particular application.

Because of the complexity of the devices, programming of them is undertaken using CAD techniques, the computer also driving an appropriate hardware programmer. Software is either supplied by the foundry or, more recently, available from independent software groups that allow programming of devices from a range of vendors. The hardware programmer often has to be personalized (at extra cost), so that it applies the

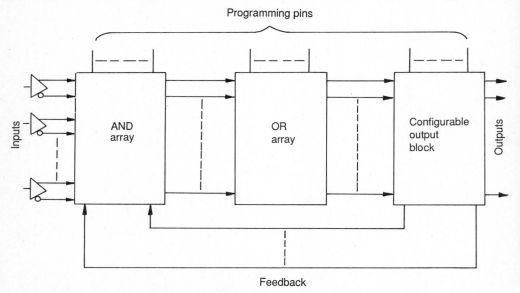

Figure 7.2 Basic structure of a programmable logic array

correct voltages and timing information to hardware program the chip. Most software will run on an IBM clone as well as the more expensive class of workstation. The hardware programmer is similar to a general purpose EPROM programmer and in some cases can be the same unit.

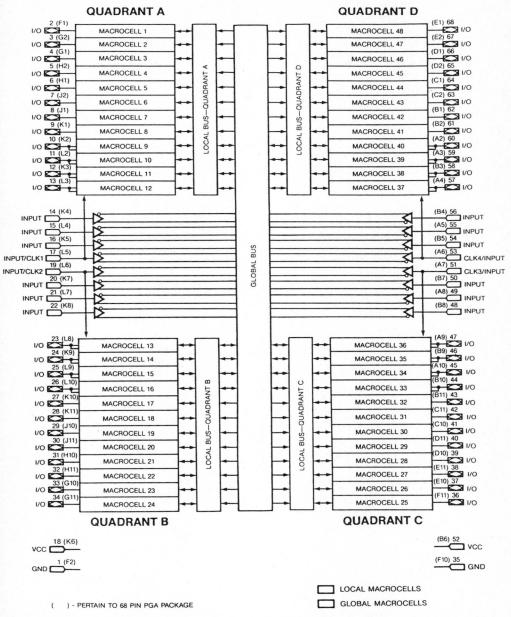

Figure 7.3 Block diagram of the Altera EP1800 'programmable gate array'. Reprinted with the permission of Altera Corporation.

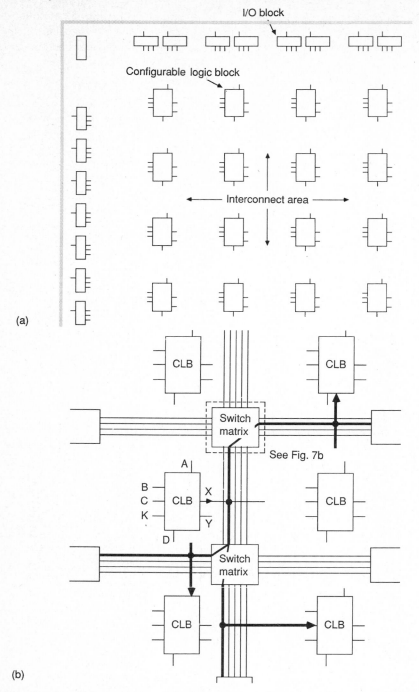

Figure 7.4 (a) Logic cell array structure, (b) The switching matrix to route interconnections (Xilinx, 1986)

The design strategy is similar to that for a semi-custom design. There is initially a design phase where the designer feeds into the computer the schematic diagram, a state diagram or a truth table. Textual as well as circuit diagram inputs can be used. The design is verified using a simulator, and test vectors can be generated. If the design is correct, then the file for the hardware programmer is generated, down-loaded and the chip programmed. The completed chip can either be tested using the test vectors generated or in circuit, in the actual product. Should an error be made, then with an erasable PLA the device can be erased and reprogrammed correctly.

7.4   Programmable gate arrays

Several PLD types are called programmable gate arrays. Their structure can be similar to the PLAs previously discussed or completely different. An example of the former is the Altera structure shown in Figure 7.3. It consists of an array of simple PLDs called macrocells, interconnected by an internal bus structure.

In the case of the Xilinx logic cell array (LCA), the structure is similar to the block layout gate array (Figure 3.7(a)). There are two significant differences. First, the blocks are not simple gate structures, but quite complex function blocks. Second, the routing between blocks is already built into the chip using electronic switching to route the desired path. Figure 7.4(a) shows the layout of a logic cell array, while Figure 7.4(b) indicates how the routing is achieved (Xilinx, 1986).

The configurable logic blocks are in effect individual PLAs. They can accept up to four logic inputs and generate up to two outputs. One output may be programmed to come via a flip-flop. Feedback is also allowed. Figure 7.5(a) shows in block diagram form a configurable logic block.

The input–output block is similar to that used in a PLA, in that it can be set up as an input, or output pad, and in the case of the latter, the option of being either a normal or tristate output pad. A block diagram representation is given in Figure 7.5(b).

As with some of the more specialized PLA chips, additional functions may be included, for example, a crystal oscillated circuit and a battery back-up mode to conserve power.

Another difference between these devices and the conventional PLA is the method of characterization. The blocks and routing are configured using dynamic memory elements. Thus, if power is turned off the stored pattern is lost. To overcome this difficulty, the characterizing details are down loaded each time power is restored. It can be either from a computer or from an onboard dedicated EPROM. The time taken to reconfigure after the power is turned on is typically 15 milliseconds.

Programming of these devices is achieved in a similar way to a normal PLA. However, each block must be individually configured. Input information to a logic block is presented either as a Boolean algebra expression, Karnough map or cell library information that is called up. A software library allows groups of blocks to be quickly configured for all the normal standard functions including counters, shift registers, and arithmetic logic units. Since the file specifying the configuration is to be written into an EPROM, only a normal EPROM hardware programmer is required.

The programmable gate array devices are a very powerful set of chips that can perform identical functions to standard gate arrays. With gate counts up to 3000 being presently available, they will compete directly with small standard gate arrays. Other advantages include no non-return engineering costs, and programming is fast and inexpensive. Unfortunately for many applications the PLD may be too expensive.

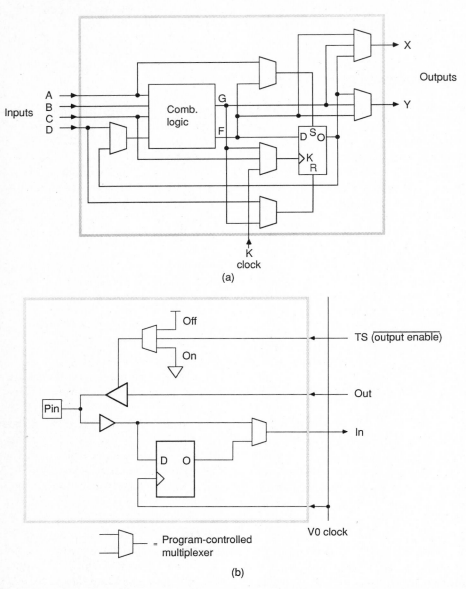

Figure 7.5 Block diagrams of (a) the configurable logic circuit, and (b) input-output circuit for a programmable gate array (Xilinx, 1986)

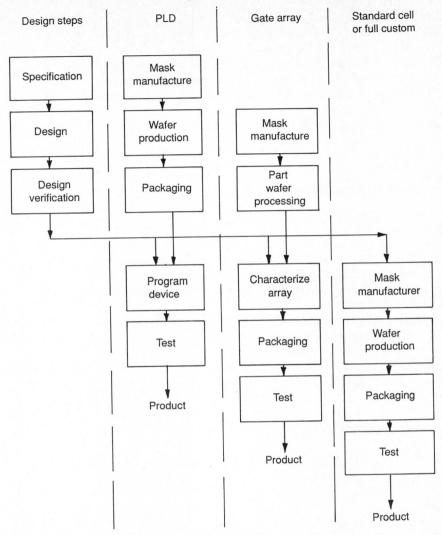

Figure 7.6 Comparison of programmable logic devices with other manufacturing methods

7.5 Questions

1. What advantages can programmable logic devices offer manufacturers for:
   (a) small lot run products?
   (b) products having very large production volumes?
2. In what way does the structure of a programmable logic device differ from a read only memory chip?

3. Some people believe that programmable logic devices should rightly be called ACICs while others strongly disagree. Prepare a table listing the arguments for and against.

4. Various physical methods are used to program programmable logic devices, including anti-fuses. These consist of two plates separated by a low breakdown dielectric (similar to a capacitor). Application of a voltage, typically 20 volts, causes a breakdown and the plates become permanently short circuited. What advantages do you believe anti-fuse methods have over the following alternatives?
   (a) polysilicon fuses
   (b) dynamic programming
   (c) ultraviolet erasable systems.

7.6   Bibliography

Altera (1988). *1988 Databook*, September, p.11.

Agrowal, O. P. & Laws, D. A. (1984). 'The role of programmable logic in system design', *VLSI Design*, vol. 5, March, p.44–50.

Cole, B. C. (1987). 'Programmable logic devices: Faster, denser and a lot more of them', *Electronics*, vol. 35, 17 September, p.61–4.

DATA I/O (1986). *Programmable Logic, A Basic Guide for the Designer*, 2nd edition, Data I/O Corporation, Redmond, USA.

Elektor (1985). 'Programmable array logic', *Elektor*, vol. 11, May, p.52–9.

Hinder, V. L. & Rappaport, A. S. (1987). 'Employing semicustom: A study of users and potential users', *VLSI System Design*, vol. 8, 20 May, p.6–25.

Signetics (1976). *Field Programmable Logic Arrays*, Signetics Corporation, California, USA.

Xilinx (1986). *The Programmable Gate Array Design Handbook*, Xilinx Inc., San Jose, USA.

7.7   Selected vendors

Actel Semiconductors Corp.
Advanced Micro Devices Inc.
Altera Corporation
Atmel Corp.
Cypress Semiconductor
Exel Microelectronics Inc.
Gazelle Microcircuits Inc.
Gould Semiconductors Inc.
Harris Semiconductors
Intel Corp.
Lattice Semiconductor Corp.
Monolithic Memories Inc.
National/Fairchild

Panatech Semiconductors
Philips/Signetics
PLX Technology
Samsung Semiconductor Inc.
Seeq Technology Inc.
Seiko Semiconductor Ltd
SGS/Thompson
Sprague Solid State
Texas Instruments Inc.
VLSI Technology Inc.
Wafer Scale Integration Inc.
Xilinx Incorporated

8 Educational gate arrays

8.1 Introduction

In many educational establishments, training for integrated circuit design has been based on full custom design using multi-project chips. Training in semicustom design and particularly gate arrays has the problem that there is really no low-cost gate array system directly applicable to training. What is required is a semicustom service that can accommodate a large number of student designs at low cost. There are four possibilities:

1. To use a commercially available gate array and allocate each student a number of gates. The difficulty is that there are insufficient pads available and frequently those that are assigned to students can be separated by several projects and thus there is a routing problem.
2. To use a commercially available gate array and break it down into several identical areas, for example quarters. A group of students is assigned an area and they are responsible for a reasonably large project. The difficulty with this scheme is that if one student makes an error then the work of many students is ruined. Further, students cannot identify their design and individually test it.
3. Make use of commercially available programmable gate array logic chips.
4. Design a special semicustom chip that is suitable for training—a multi-project gate array chip.

The last two alternatives are most attractive and will be discussed further.

8.2 Programmable gate arrays

As discussed in Section 7.4, programmable gate arrays are not strictly ASICs, yet they do offer an economical method of training. Since the dynamic switch settings for the arrays are stored in an EPROM, it is a simple matter to produce, in quantity, printed circuit experiment boards with the gate array package permanently wired to an appropriate socket for testing and a low insertion socket to take the EPROM. Such a unit provides a very flexible system for digital training.

Unfortunately programmable gate arrays have two limitations. First, the arrays are set up to be used with a suite of design software, including automatic routing. Students are too far removed from the silicon technology and, while they may produce working circuits, the skill that they develop is simply the manipulation of software.

Second, the function blocks available are complex and, without the software support, excess time is required for training. Perhaps training in programmable gate arrays or programmable logic devices should be given simply as an indication of how small-system prototyping can be achieved.

8.3   Special gate arrays

The philosophy employed here is to allow students to design semi-manually a simple gate array circuit, so that they can quickly appreciate the technology, both silicon technology and computer aided design methods. Normally a simple cell design, such as a JK flip-flop, built from primitive gates is sufficient.

The difficulty with a commercial gate array is that it is designed to implement a large system. What is required for training is an array of small gate arrays on a single chip. The inclusion of many input-output pads consumes considerable silicon area and so a pad-sharing technique has been developed. Buffers are not included on chip, but are placed on the test board. In this way, the silicon area is used efficiently.

It should be noted that the pads are made using the metal characterization layer so that their number can be adjusted to give some students access to more gates.

The next sections describe three types of educational gate arrays. Layouts for the basic cells are given in CIF in Appendix 2, together with technical data for simulation purposes.

While these educational gate arrays have been used for training undergraduate students, it should be pointed out that they are equally applicable for training industrial engineers and used by industry for prototyping circuits.

A special layout and simulation software package has been developed for two of the educational gate arrays, and is available on disk. The disk also includes the CIF files for the arrays. The software runs on an IBM (or clone) personal computer, having a color monitor and EGA card, two button mouse and at least 640 bytes of RAM. A hard disk machine is preferable. The software is suitable for students to design their own gate arrays. Merging of the arrays into a large chip for processing must be undertaken on a more advanced workstation.

The software was developed in conjunction with Singapore Polytechnic under the Australian ASEAN Economic Co-operative Programme Microelectrics Project.

Copies of the disk are available to recognized educational establishments for a nominal charge of A$60 to cover costs. Applications must be on letterhead paper and enclose a money order or check made out to Australian Silicon Technology, and mailed to:

> Educational Gate Array Disk
> Australian Silicon Technology
> Techsearch Incorporated
> 183 Melbourne Street
> NORTH ADELAIDE
> SA   AUSTRALIA   5006

Other interested bodies can also apply, however, they should first make enquiries about the charge before forwarding any money.

8.3.1 An IIL educational array

Figure 8.1 shows the 5×5 mm square gate array chip. It consists of a matrix of 7×7 individual arrays with each column of seven arrays being powered separately. Two ring oscillators are included for assessment of chip performance.

Each of up to 49 students has for use twenty 3-output collector IIL gates and eight input/output pads. The students characterize their array using three masks: a shallow N-mask used for the collectors of the gates and cross unders, a contact cut mask, and an interconnection metal mask. Figure 8.2 shows a single student gate array in its two versions, horizontal and vertical. A grid can be called from the library to assist in the routing of the array.

A typical classroom situation might be as follows. Students on course receive seven hours of tuition on ASICs, three hours of tutorials on the software that they will use, and have ten hours to design and test their gate arrays. Normally eight hours are required for the design and two hours for testing.

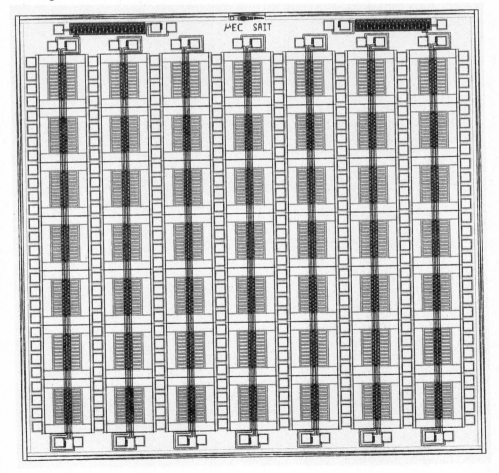

Figure 8.1   Complete IIL educational gate array

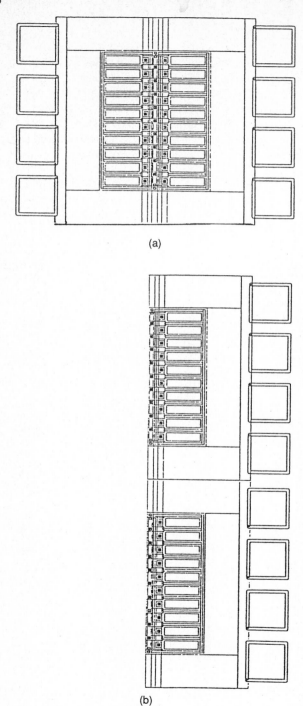

(a)

(b)

Figure 8.2 Individual student gate array: (a) horizontal, (b) vertical

The design process is an iterative one, consisting of four steps. Initially, an IIL schematic diagram is determined, one that will perform the set exercise function. This is then confirmed by SPICE simulation, using the simple model shown in Figure 8.3.

If correct, a layout is undertaken using either a textual or iterative entry software package. All routing is done using 8 μm wired metal on 16 μm grid spacing. Important parasitic elements are extracted manually (Figure 8.4) and a new simulation undertaken.

Depending on where the base and collector contacts are positioned, as well as on the number of collector contacts to a logic gate, an appropriate dynamic model is selected for the complete function and timing simulation (Figure 8.5).

Students work in pairs on the same project with one student producing a horizontal layout and the other a vertical. A typical project may be:

1. Two to four bit decoder with enable
2. One bit expandable arithmetic add subtract unit
3. One bit expandable ALU ($A+B$, $\bar{B}$, $A+\bar{B}$, $A\oplus B$)
4. Four to one multiplexer with enable
5. Expandable two bit odd parity generator
6. Expandable two bit magnitude comparator $A < B$, $A = B$
7. JK type flip-flop with preset and clear
8. D type flip-flop with preset and clear
9. Expandable two bit binary ripple up counter
10. Expandable one bit parallel load shift register.

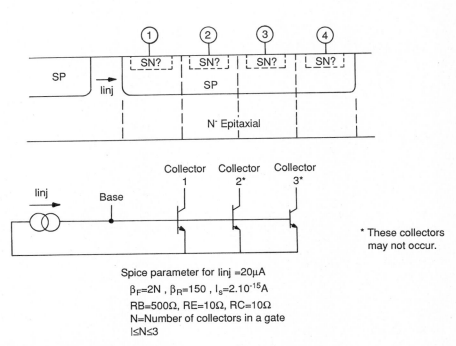

Spice parameter for linj =20μA

β_F=2N , β_R=150 , I_s=2.10^{-15}A

RB=500Ω, RE=10Ω, RC=10Ω
N=Number of collectors in a gate
1≤N≤3

Figure 8.3 Simple static IIL gate model

Once designs are completed they are merged and sent for fabrication. The dice are packaged in 40-pin DIL packages. This allows no more than four student designs in a single column to be bonded out in a single package.

Testing is undertaken on a standard experiment board, shown in Figure 8.6. It has four input/output buffers, four LED indicators and provides a range of injection currents. SPICE parameters are given for 20 μA injection currents, and the range available allows students to plot speed of operation against injection current. The input/output buffer circuit and associated wiring stray capacities are shown in Figure 8.7. Students are given these figures before designing their array so they can form part of the simulation.

Underpasses

Resistances   Contact cut resistance (NC)   5 ohm
              SN diffusion   5 ohm/square

Capacitance   Side wall $2.95 \ 10^{-3}$ pF/μm
              Area $0.581 \ 10^{-3}$ pF/μm²

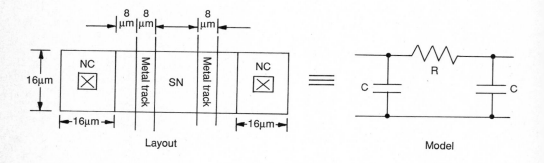

Layout   Model

Underpass going under N° tracks	R ohms	C pF
1	18	0.47
2	23	0.60
3	28	0.72
4	33	0.84

Metal interconnection
   Resistance   0.05 ohm/square
   Capacity $5.0 \ 10^{-5}$ pF/μm²

For 8μm wide tracks
   Resistance/μm 6.25 m ohm (normally ignore as resistance so low)
   Capacitance/μm 4.10^{-4} pF

Figure 8.4   Important parasitic components and models

This gate array has been used on several occasions with great success. Students were most enthusiastic. At least 65 percent of designs performed to specification. Figure 8.8 shows a merged gate array containing forty-nine student designs.

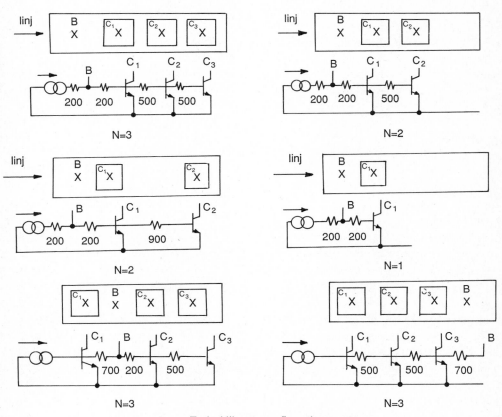

Typical IIL gate configurations

Spice parameters for IIL gate transistors (NPN)
linj=20µ amps

Note: N=NPN collectors (transistors) in a gate

IS=2E-15 amps	CJE=0.19pF
BF=2N	VJE=0.65 volts
BR=150	MJE=0.4
RB=500 ohms	CJC=0.37pF
RE=10 ohms	VJC=0.70 volts
RC=10 ohms	MJC=0.33

Figure 8.5 Dynamic models for an IIL gate

8.3.2   An nMOS educational gate array

The system proposed is really a pseudo nMOS educational gate array in that the load device is a P-channel enhancement rather than an N-channel depletion field effect transistor. It can be fabricated on a 2-micron double metal P-well CMOS process. Figure 8.9 shows a small array while Appendix 2 gives the CIF file for a single cell.

This gate is laid out as an array of the size that is deemed satisfactory. Pads need have no on-chip buffering, but should be ESD protected. Like the previous IIL gate array, the experiment board shown in Figure 8.6 can be used for testing.

8.3.3   A CMOS educational gate array

Figure 8.10 shows the basic CMOS educational gate array cell. It consists of eight pads with ESD protection, and ten 3-input and ten 2-input CMOS gates. The transistors are all unconnected so that the cells can be configured to be NAND, NOR or inverter circuits.

Appendix 2 gives the CIF file and other information for this cell. Like the previous educational gate arrays it can be assembled into an array of any preferred size. Figure 8.11 shows a small educational array for eight students. It can be fabricated in a 3-micron double metal P-well CMOS process. Testing of the array can be undertaken using the experiment board shown in Figure 8.6.

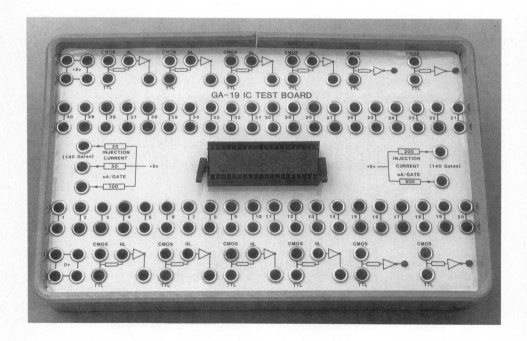

Figure 8.6   Standard educational gate array test board

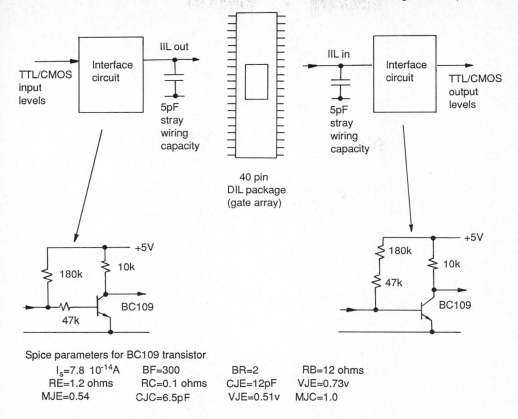

Figure 8.7 Interfacing to the IIL educational gate array

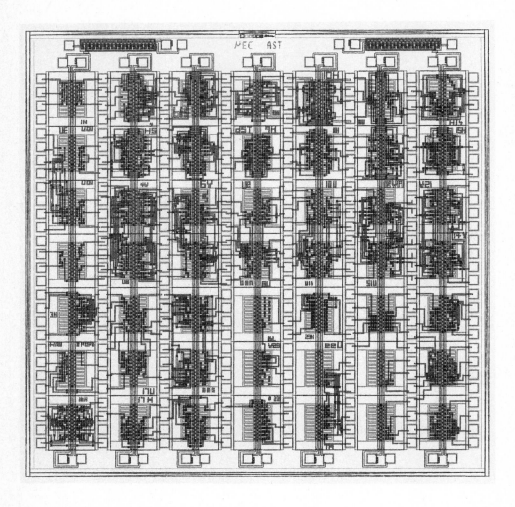

Figure 8.8   Completed student gate array containing forty-nine designs

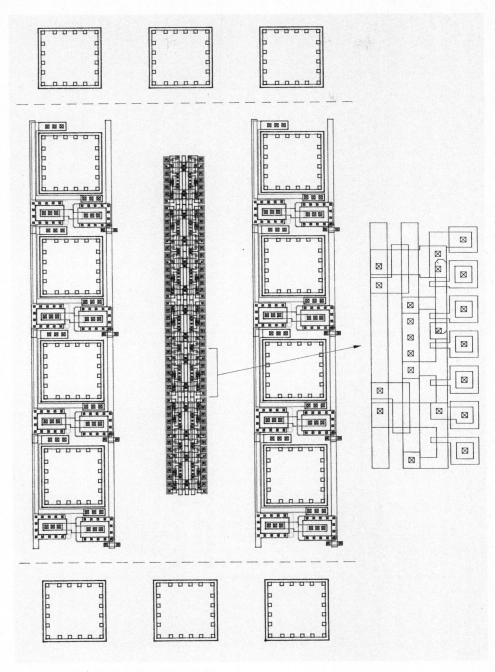

Figure 8.9   A pseudo nMOS gate array

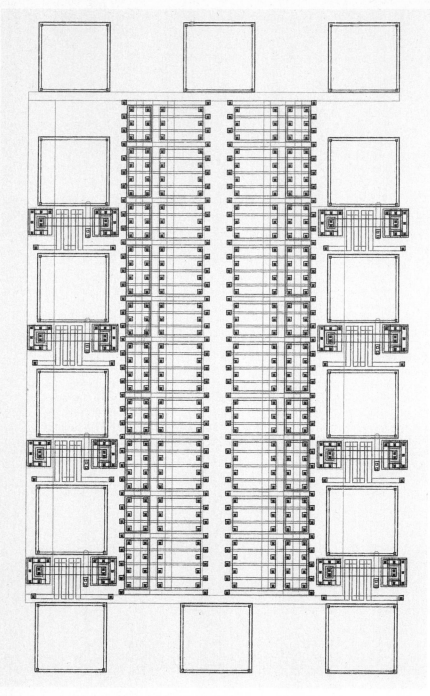

Figure 8.10   Basic CMOS student gate array cell

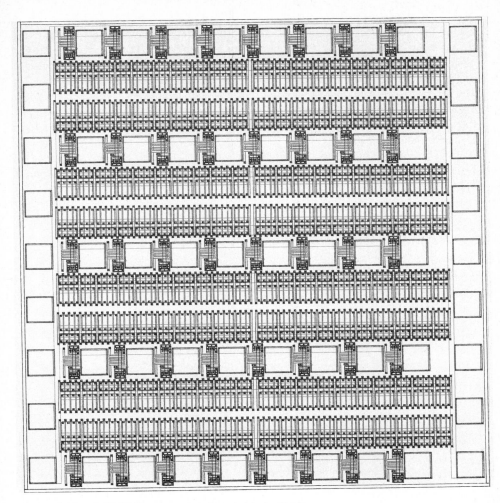

Figure 8.11 A CMOS gate array for eight students

8.4 Conclusion

Only brief descriptions of the educational arrays have been provided to establish the concept. The idea is relevant not only for undergraduate, but also for industrial training. While one may laugh at a design consisting of only twenty gates, it is sufficient to establish concepts and give the student confidence. It should also be pointed out that, since the pad metal is of the same layer as that used for the characterization of the array, students can be allocated as many gate blocks as they require. Thus for the IIL array given in Figure 8.1, students could be assigned two blocks, a whole column of seven blocks, two columns or even the whole array of 980 gates (Haskard, 1988).

8.5   Questions

1. Figure 8.6 shows the experiment board used for testing educational gate array chips packaged in a 40-pin DIL. If dynamic reprogrammable PLDs are used for various student laboratory experiments, design the layout for a suitable general purpose experimental board. The PLD comes in 48-pin DIL and the associated EPROM in 24-pin DIL packages. A low insertion force socket should be used for the latter.
2. Examine the IIL gate array chip layout given in Figure 8.2(a). Complete the layout of the chip for:
   (a) an exclusive OR gate
   (b) a D type edge trigger flip-flop with reset
3. Repeat question 2 above, but for the CMOS educational gate array shown in Figures 3.5 and 8.10.

8.6   Bibliography

Haskard, M. R. (1988). 'Multi-project gate array system for educational purposes', *Journal of Semi-Custom Integrated Circuits*, vol. 6, December, p.27–30.

APPENDIX 1: Standard cell library

A1.1 Digital cells

Code	Cell name
Logic gates	
INV1	Single inverter
INV2	Dual inverter
INV4	Quad inverter
AND2	Two input AND gate
AND3	Three input AND gate
AND4	Four input AND gate
AND8	Eight input AND gate
NAND2	Two input NAND gate
NAND3	Three input NAND gate
NAND4	Four input NAND gate
NAND8	Eight input NAND gate
OR2	Two input OR gate
OR3	Three input OR gate
OR4	Four input OR gate
OR8	Eight input OR gate
NOR2	Two input NOR gate
NOR3	Three input NOR gate
NOR4	Four input NOR gate
NOR8	Eight input NOR gate
AOI22	Two AND two input and OR invert gate
AOI32	Three AND two input and OR invert gate
AOI42	Four AND two input and OR invert gate
AOI23	Two AND three input and OR invert gate
AOI24	Two AND four input and OR invert gate
EXOR	Exclusive OR gate
EXNOR	Exclusive NOR gate

All of the above gates can be designed with complementary outputs. The code is the same except a C is added to the end of the code.

BUF4	Non inverting buffer 4X drive
BUF8	Non inverting buffer 8X drive

IBUF4	Inverting buffer 4X drive
IBUF8	Inverting buffer 8X drive
BUF4C	Buffer complementary output 4X drive
BUF8C	Buffer complementary output 8X drive

Special logic functions

Code	Cell name
ADFUL	Full adder
ALU	Arithmetic logic unit
SCHT	Schmitt trigger
MUX2	Two to one multiplexer
MUX4	Four to one multiplexer
PAR2	Two bit parity generator
PAR4	Four bit parity generator
DEC4	Two to four decoder
DEC8	Three to eight decoder

Bistable devices

Code	Cell name
CCND	Cross coupled NAND latch
CCNR	Cross coupled NOR latch
GRSFF	Gated RS flip-flop
DFF	D type flip-flop
DFFR	D type flip-flop with reset
DDFFSR	D type flip-flop with set and reset
JKFF	JK type flip-flop
JKFFR	JK flip-flop with reset
JKFFSR	JK flip-flop with set and reset
UDC	Two stage up down counter with reset
UDCS	Two stage up down counter parallel load and reset
SHR	Two bit shift register
SHRLR	Two bit shift left shift right shift register
SHRP	Two bit shift register parallel load
SHRLRP	Two bit shift left/right register parallel load

A1.2   Analog cells

Code	Cell name
OPAP	Operational amplifier single power rail
OPAP2	Operational amplifier split power rail
OPAPP	High drive capacity operational amplifier single power rail
OPAMP2	High drive capacity operational amplifier split power supply
OPAML	Low gain operational amplifier single supply

OPAML2	Low gain operational amplifier split supply
COMP	Comparator single supply
COMP2	Comparator split supply
VREF	Voltage reference
VVREF	Variable voltage reference
VCO	Voltage controlled oscillator
PPL	Phase locked loop
MUX2	Two input analog multiplexer
MUX4	Four input analog multiplexer
LDTH	Single vertical wire lead through
DTOA4	Four bit digital to analog converter
DTOA8	Eight bit digital to analog converter

A1.3 Pads

Code	Cell name
PDIN	Input pad with protection
PDDINB	Digital input pad with protection and buffering
PPDINC	Digital input pad with protection and buffered complementary outputs
PDDOT	Digital output pad
PDDOTT	Tristate digital output pad
PDAOTV	Analog voltage output pad
PDAOTI	Analog current output pad
PDVREF	Variable voltage reference pad or pad pair
PDTST	Monitor test point pad
PDMT	Empty pad
PDCR	Corner pad
PDBLK	Blank pad

APPENDIX 2:
Educational
gate array data

A2.1 IIL gate array

The CIF file for the layout of this educational gate array, together with appropriate software for layout and simulation, are available to educational establishments at a nominal charge to cover expenses. See Section 8.3 for details.

A2.1.1 Layout rules

Figure A.1 gives the dimensions in microns for half of the IIL educational gate array. This information is helpful if the layout is to be undertaken manually.

The layout of the array is on a 16 micron grid. Figure A.2 provides a summary of the layout rules.

A2.1.2 Generation of the gate model

Because the designer has freedom both in locating the position of the base and collector contacts and the number of collector contacts per gate, each gate requires its own model. The gate layout can be subdivided into several basic elemental cells. These can be assembled in various ways to form the appropriate model for any gate configuration. Figure A.3 gives the elemental cells and illustrates how they are assembled to generate models for a range of gates. Table A.1 provides the SPICE data for a typical 8 micron bipolar process.

Table A.1 SPICE parameters for the IIL gate array NPN transistors with a gate injection current of 20 microamps. N is the number of NPN collectors (transistors) to a gate

IS=2.E-15 amps	BF=2N	BR=150	RB=500 ohms
RE=10 ohms	RC=10 ohms	CJE=0.19 pF	VJE=0.65 volts
MJE=0.4	CJC=0.37 pF	VJC=0.70 volts	MJC=0.33

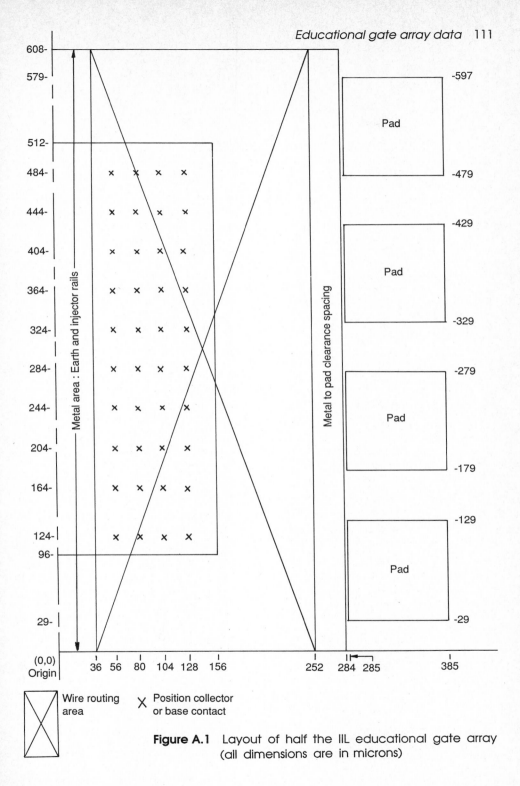

Figure A.1 Layout of half the IIL educational gate array (all dimensions are in microns)

Contacts

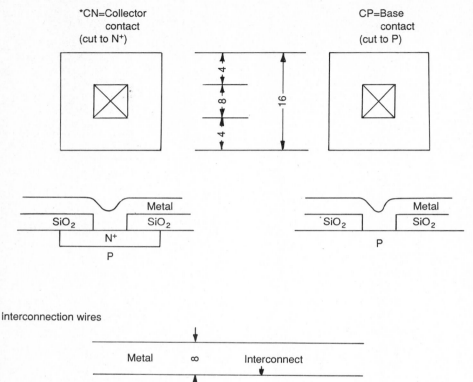

interconnection wires

Crossunders

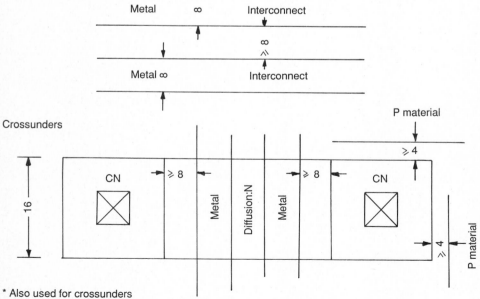

* Also used for crossunders

Figure A.2   Layout rules for the gate array (all dimensions are in microns)

Elemental cells

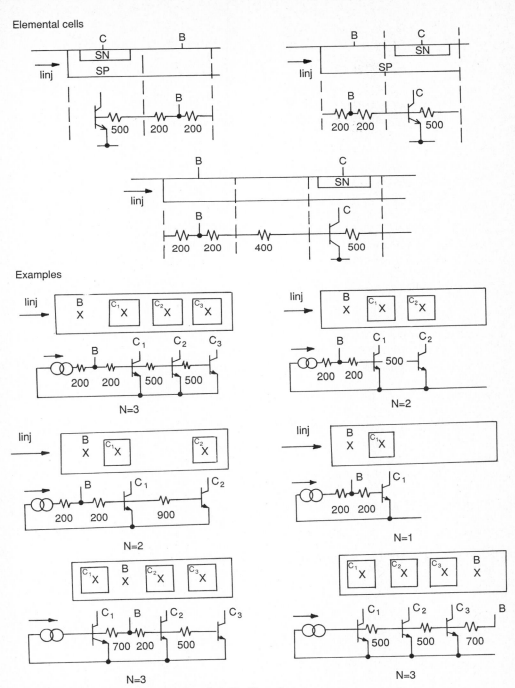

Examples

Figure A.3 Development of models for IIL gates

A2.1.3 CIF code for the IIL gate array

(CIF file of symbol hierarchy rooted at mpc_cell.k);
DS 2 1 1;
9 gates.k;
L DN;
B 3100 400 27550 49900;
B 13700 600 32850 50400;
B 13700 600 32850 10400;
B 3100 400 27550 10900;
B 1000 38600 26200 30400;
B 1000 38600 24200 30400;
B 7800 1400 25200 46400;
B 7800 1400 25200 42400;
B 7800 1400 25200 38400;
B 7800 1400 25200 34400;
B 7800 1400 25200 30400;
B 7800 1400 25200 26400;
B 7800 1400 25200 22400;
B 7800 1400 25200 18400;
B 7800 1400 25200 14400;
B 600 40600 10400 30400;
B 600 40600 40000 30400;
B 3100 400 22850 49900;
B 13700 600 17550 50400;
B 10600 600 16000 18400;
B 10600 600 16000 14400;
B 10600 600 16000 22400;
B 10600 600 16000 26400;
B 10600 600 16000 30400;
B 10600 600 16000 34400;
B 10600 600 16000 38400;
B 10600 600 16000 42400;
B 10600 600 16000 46400;
B 10600 600 34400 18400;
B 10600 600 34400 14400;
B 10600 600 34400 22400;
B 10600 600 34400 26400;
B 10600 600 34400 30400;
B 10600 600 34400 34400;
B 10600 600 34400 38400;
B 10600 600 34400 42400;
B 10600 600 34400 46400;
B 13700 600 17550 10400;
B 3100 400 22850 10900;
L SP;

Table A.3 SPICE parameters for a 2-micron CMOS process
(*Micro Circuit Engineering*)

N-channel transistor

VTO	= 0.86702	volts	GAMMA	= 0.31844	$V**1/2$
DELTA	= 3.7029	—	NSU	= 19.406	$E15/cm^3$
XJ	= 0.15000	microns	TOX	= 325.00	Angstrom
LD	= 0.14523	microns	UO	= 699.99	$cm^2/V.S$
UCRIT	= 59.401	E3 V/cm	UEXP	= 0.13242	—
VMAX	= 50.630	E3 m/sec	NEFF	= 3.1363	—
LAMBDA	= 3.75320E-02	1/volts	PHI	= 0.79999	volts
PB	= 0.80000	volts	NFS	= 9.8784	$E9/cm**2$
KP	= 53.010	$E-6 A/V^2$			

P-channel transistor

VTO	= -0.97917	volts	GAMMA	= 0.49997	$V**1/2$
DELTA	= 1.3994	—	NSUB	= 19.234	$E15/cm^3$
XJ	= 0.30000	microns	TOX	= 325.00	Angstrom
LD	= 0.12064	microns	UO	= 300.00	$cm^2/V.S$
UCRIT	= 14.878	E3 V/cm	UEXP	= 0.16588	—
VMAX	= 50.013	E3 m/sec	NEFF	= 4.2317	—
LAMBDA	= 4.56120E-02	1/volts	PHI	= 0.50009	volts
PB	= 0.80000	volts	NFS	= 0.59460	$E9/cm**2$
KP	= 18.743	$E-6 A/V^2$			

A2.2.3 CIF code for the pseudo nMOS educational array

(CIF file of symbol hierarchy rooted at ps_array.k);
DS 2 1 1;
9 padblank.k;
L PW;
B 11000 11000 5500 5500;
L NW;
L PY;
L NI;
L PI;
L M1;
B 11000 11000 5500 5500;
L CC;
L M2;
B 11000 11000 5500 5500;
L V1;
B 600 600 800 2900;
B 600 600 800 4650;
B 600 600 800 6400;
B 600 600 800 8150;
B 600 600 2900 800;
B 600 600 4650 800;

B 600 600 6400 800;
B 600 600 8150 800;
B 600 600 10200 2900;
B 600 600 10200 4650;
B 600 600 10200 6400;
B 600 600 10200 8150;
B 600 600 2900 10200;
B 600 600 4650 10200;
B 600 600 6400 10200;
B 600 600 8150 10200;
B 600 600 800 800;
B 600 600 10200 800;
B 600 600 10200 10200;
B 600 600 800 10200;
L GZ;
B 10000 10000 5500 5500;
L TX;
L DRC;
DF;
DS 4 1 1;
9 32nor.k;
L PW;
L NW;
L PY;
B 1800 600 1750 1050;
B 200 700 8050 2450;
B 200 700 3500 2450;
B 200 700 4600 2450;
B 200 700 5950 2450;
B 1000 1000 650 3300;
B 200 700 2300 2450;
B 600 950 6250 475;
B 600 950 2350 475;
B 1850 600 6875 1050;
B 1000 1000 1950 3300;
B 1000 1000 3250 3300;
B 1000 1000 4550 3300;
B 1000 1000 5850 3300;
B 1000 1000 7150 3300;
B 1000 1000 8450 3300;
L NI;
B 900 1800 1500 900;
B 1150 550 1475 2025;
B 450 850 3025 1925;
B 600 600 3100 1400;
B 500 700 5450 2000;

```
B 600 600 5500 1400;
B 600 600 4050 2400;
B 600 600 7000 2400;
B 900 2400 7150 1200;
B 8200 400 5000 2500;
B 400 850 8900 1925;
B 600 600 8800 1400;
L PI;
B 1800 600 4300 1400;
L M1;
B 600 600 4050 2400;
W 400 3950 2500 1600 2500;
B 600 900 650 3150;
B 1700 600 1200 2400;
B 600 600 7000 2400;
B 600 600 1950 3300;
B 600 600 3250 3300;
B 600 600 4550 3300;
B 600 600 5850 3300;
B 600 600 7150 3300;
B 600 600 8450 3300;
B 450 350 7075 2875;
B 9100 600 4550 1400;
B 9100 600 4550 300;
L CC;
B 200 200 7000 2400;
B 200 200 4900 1400;
B 200 200 4300 1400;
B 200 200 3700 1400;
B 200 200 3100 1400;
B 200 200 5500 1400;
B 200 200 4050 2400;
B 200 200 1750 2400;
B 200 200 1200 2400;
B 200 200 650 3300;
B 200 200 7000 300;
B 200 200 6250 300;
B 200 200 2350 300;
B 200 200 1650 300;
B 200 200 1950 3300;
B 200 200 3250 3300;
B 200 200 4550 3300;
B 200 200 5850 3300;
B 200 200 7150 3300;
B 200 200 8450 3300;
B 200 200 8800 1400;
```

```
L M2;
L V1;
L GZ;
L TX;
L DRC;
DF;
DS 3 1 1;
9 32nor_array.k;
C 4 R -1 0 T 54600 600;
C 4 MX T 54600 0;
C 4 T 54600 0;
C 4 MY T 54600 600;
C 4 MX T 36400 0;
C 4 R -1 0 T 36400 600;
C 4 T 36400 0;
C 4 MY T 36400 600;
C 4 MX T 18200 0;
C 4 R -1 0 T 18200 600;
C 4 T 18200 0;
C 4 MY T 18200 600;
C 4 MY T 0 600;
C 4 T 0 0;
L PW;
L NW;
L PY;
L NI;
L PI;
L M1;
L CC;
L M2;
L V1;
L GZ;
L TX;
L DRC;
DF;
DS 5 1 1;
9 pad.k;
L PW;
B 2800 4950 16750 3425;
B 11000 11000 7700 7100;
L NW;
L PY;
B 600 2750 20050 13725;
B 14050 800 7325 700;
B 800 11500 13950 6850;
B 1200 3750 14150 10725;
```

B 1500 6050 1050 3325;
L NI;
B 1200 3350 16750 3425;
W 800 19050 13650 19050 7900 15450 7900 15450 13650 19050 13650;
L PI;
W 800 18550 6300 18550 550 14950 550 14950 6300 18550 6300;
B 1200 3350 17250 10775;
L M1;
B 20650 950 10325 475;
B 600 600 20050 14800;
B 20650 950 10325 13725;
B 1700 800 17000 7100;
B 1200 5350 17250 9775;
B 1200 5350 16750 4425;
B 800 4750 14950 3225;
B 800 5450 18550 2875;
B 1200 3750 14150 10725;
B 800 5450 19050 11325;
B 800 4750 15450 10975;
B 600 600 20050 12650;
B 11000 11000 7700 7100;
B 1500 4750 1050 3975;
L CC;
B 200 200 20050 14800;
B 300 300 14950 1650;
B 300 300 14950 2850;
B 300 300 14950 4000;
B 300 300 14950 5150;
B 300 300 14950 550;
B 300 300 16150 550;
B 300 300 17350 550;
B 300 300 18550 550;
B 300 300 18550 1650;
B 300 300 18550 2850;
B 300 300 18550 4000;
B 300 300 18550 5150;
B 600 600 16750 3450;
B 600 600 16750 2350;
B 600 600 16750 4500;
B 600 600 14150 9450;
B 600 600 14150 10700;
B 600 600 14150 11950;
B 300 300 19050 12550;
B 300 300 19050 11350;
B 300 300 19050 10200;
B 300 300 19050 9050;

B 300 300 15450 12550;
B 300 300 15450 11350;
B 300 300 15450 10200;
B 300 300 15450 9050;
B 300 300 15450 13650;
B 300 300 16650 13650;
B 300 300 17850 13650;
B 300 300 19050 13650;
B 200 200 20050 12650;
B 600 600 17250 10800;
B 600 600 17250 9700;
B 600 600 17250 11850;
B 600 600 1050 3100;
B 600 600 1050 4350;
B 600 600 1050 5600;
L M2;
B 11000 11000 7700 7100;
L V1;
B 600 600 10300 2400;
B 600 600 8550 2400;
B 600 600 6800 2400;
B 600 600 5050 2400;
B 600 600 12400 4500;
B 600 600 12400 6250;
B 600 600 12400 8000;
B 600 600 12400 9750;
B 600 600 10300 11800;
B 600 600 8550 11800;
B 600 600 6800 11800;
B 600 600 5050 11800;
B 600 600 3000 4500;
B 600 600 3000 6250;
B 600 600 3000 8000;
B 600 600 3000 9750;
B 600 600 12400 2400;
B 600 600 12400 11800;
B 600 600 3000 11800;
B 600 600 3000 2400;
L GZ;
B 10000 10000 7700 7100;
L TX;
L DRC;
DF;
DS 6 1 1;
9 padin.k;
L PW;

B 11000 11000 5500 5500;
B 4950 2800 1825 -3550;
L NW;
B 4950 2800 9175 -4050;
L PY;
B 6050 1500 1725 12150;
B 3750 1200 9125 -950;
B 11500 800 5250 -750;
B 800 14050 -900 5875;
B 2750 600 12125 -6850;
L NI;
W 800 12050 -5850 12050 -2250 6300 -2250 6300 -5850 12050 -5850;
B 3350 1200 1825 -3350;
L PI;
B 3350 1200 9175 -4050;
W 800 4700 -5350 4700 -1750 -1050 -1750 -1050 -5350 4700 -5350;
L M1;
B 4750 1500 2375 12150;
B 11000 11000 5500 5500;
B 600 600 11050 -6850;
B 4750 800 9375 -2250;
B 5450 800 9725 -5850;
B 3750 1200 9125 -950;
B 5450 800 1275 -5350;
B 4750 800 1625 -1750;
B 5350 1200 2825 -3350;
B 5350 1200 8175 -4050;
B 800 1700 5500 -3800;
B 950 20650 12125 2875;
B 600 600 13200 -6850;
B 950 20650 -1125 2875;
L CC;
B 600 600 4000 12150;
B 600 600 2750 12150;
B 600 600 1500 12150;
B 600 600 10250 -4050;
B 600 600 8100 -4050;
B 600 600 9200 -4050;
B 200 200 11050 -6850;
B 300 300 12050 -5850;
B 300 300 12050 -4650;
B 300 300 12050 -3450;
B 300 300 12050 -2250;
B 300 300 7450 -2250;
B 300 300 8600 -2250;
B 300 300 9750 -2250;

B 300 300 10950 -2250;
B 300 300 7450 -5850;
B 300 300 8600 -5850;
B 300 300 9750 -5850;
B 300 300 10950 -5850;
B 600 600 10350 -950;
B 600 600 9100 -950;
B 600 600 7850 -950;
B 600 600 2900 -3550;
B 600 600 750 -3550;
B 600 600 1850 -3550;
B 300 300 3550 -5350;
B 300 300 2400 -5350;
B 300 300 1250 -5350;
B 300 300 50 -5350;
B 300 300 -1050 -5350;
B 300 300 -1050 -4150;
B 300 300 -1050 -2950;
B 300 300 -1050 -1750;
B 300 300 3550 -1750;
B 300 300 2400 -1750;
B 300 300 1250 -1750;
B 300 300 50 -1750;
B 200 200 13200 -6850;
L M2;
B 11000 11000 5500 5500;
L V1;
B 600 600 800 10200;
B 600 600 10200 10200;
B 600 600 10200 800;
B 600 600 800 800;
B 600 600 8150 10200;
B 600 600 6400 10200;
B 600 600 4650 10200;
B 600 600 2900 10200;
B 600 600 10200 8150;
B 600 600 10200 6400;
B 600 600 10200 4650;
B 600 600 10200 2900;
B 600 600 8150 800;
B 600 600 6400 800;
B 600 600 4650 800;
B 600 600 2900 800;
B 600 600 800 8150;
B 600 600 800 6400;
B 600 600 800 4650;

```
B 600 600 800 2900;
L GZ;
B 10000 10000 5500 5500;
L TX;
L DRC;
DF;
DS 1 1 1;
9 ps_array.k;
C 2 R 0 1 T 113850 41300;
C 2 R 0 1 T 113850 21950;
C 2 R 0 1 T 113850 2600;
C 2 R 0 1 T 13600 41300;
C 2 R 0 1 T 13600 21950;
C 2 R 0 1 T 13600 2600;
C 3 R -1 0 T 87500 28150;
C 5 T 19400 39700;
C 5 T 19400 1000;
C 6 R 0 1 T 89600 41300;
C 6 R 0 1 T 70600 41300;
C 6 R 0 1 T 51600 41300;
C 6 R 0 1 T 89600 2600;
C 6 R 0 1 T 70600 2600;
C 6 R 0 1 T 51600 2600;
L PW;
L NW;
L PY;
L NI;
L PI;
L M1;
L CC;
L M2;
L V1;
L GZ;
L TX;
L DRC;
DF;
C 1;
E
```

A2.3   CMOS gate array

The CIF file for the layout of this educational gate array, together with appropriate software for layout and simulation, are available to educational establishments at a nominal charge to cover expenses. See Section 8.3 for details.

Table A.4 Resistance and capacitance of interconnection metal layers (*Micro Circuit Engineering*)

Metal Layer	Sheet resistance	Capacitance to substrate
1	0.05 ohm/square	26.E-6 pF/micron square
2	0.05 ohm/square	11.E-6 pF/micron square

A2.3.1 Layout rules

This gate array has been designed for a 3-micron, P-well, double metal process. As seen in Figure 8.10, the array consists of ten gate pairs, each pair being a 2- and a 3-input gate. Thus the total number of actual gates is twenty or twenty-five equivalent 2-input gates.

The interconnection wiring for the gates is on an 11-micron grid with a track width of 7 microns. Since the power supply rails are in metal 2, interconnection wiring running parallel to the power rails should be in metal 2. With care metal 1 may run in either direction.

A2.3.2 SPICE data

Typical values for the interconnection metal resistance and capacitance are given in Table A.4, while typical SPICE transistor model parameters are given in Table A.5.

Table A.5 SPICE parameters (*Micro Circuit Engineering*)

PARAMETER			
TYPE	PMOS	NMOS	
LEVEL		2	
VTO	-0.75	0.75	V
TOX	450	450	ANGSTROM
NSUB	60- E14	6E15	CM**-03
XJ	0.35	0.35	uM
UO	200	700	CM**2/V.S
UCRIT	1 E5	2.9E4	V/CM
UEXP	0.40	0.36	
VMAX	3.5E4	4.3E4	M/S
NEFF	3.5	4.0	
DELTA	3.0	0.2	
NFS	1 E10	1 E10	CM**-03
CJ	0.20	0.20	fF/uM**2
MJ	0.50	0.50	
CJSW	0.30	0.50	fF/uM
MJSW	0.50	0.50	
PB	0.80	0.80	V

A2.3.3 CIF code for the CMOS educational array

(CIF file of symbol hierarchy rooted at plotarray.k);
DS 3 1 1;
9 pad15.k;
L PW;
L AA;
B 700 1300 1950 13500;
B 700 1300 11750 13500;
B 2000 700 1950 11850;
B 700 3950 3300 13475;
B 700 3950 600 13475;
B 2000 700 1950 15100;
B 700 3950 10400 13475;
B 700 3950 13100 13475;
B 2000 700 11750 11850;
B 2000 700 11750 15100;
L PY;
B 700 6300 9050 14650;
B 700 6300 7950 14650;
B 700 6300 6850 14650;
B 700 6300 5750 14650;
B 1800 700 6300 11850;
B 1800 700 8500 11850;
B 1800 700 7400 17450;
B 3500 700 11150 17450;
B 4600 700 3100 17450;
L NI;
B 1200 1800 11750 13500;
B 1200 4450 3300 13475;
B 1500 1200 1950 11850;
B 1500 1200 1950 15100;
B 1200 4450 600 13475;
L PI;
B 1200 1800 1950 13500;
B 1200 4450 10400 13475;
B 1200 4450 13100 13475;
B 1500 1200 11750 15100;
B 1500 1200 11750 11850;
L M1;
B 10500 1300 6850 13500;
B 2650 700 11375 11850;
B 1300 700 12050 15100;
B 1000 3950 13200 13475;
B 1300 700 1650 15100;
B 2650 700 2325 11850;

B 1000 3950 500 13475;
B 700 700 12550 17450;
B 700 1400 4650 15200;
B 10900 10900 6850 5500;
B 700 700 1150 17450;
L CC;
B 300 300 10400 11850;
B 300 300 11750 11850;
B 300 300 13100 11850;
B 300 300 13100 13450;
B 300 300 13100 15100;
B 300 300 11750 15100;
B 300 300 600 13450;
B 300 300 1950 15100;
B 300 300 600 15100;
B 300 300 3300 11850;
B 300 300 1950 11850;
B 300 300 600 11850;
B 300 300 1950 13800;
B 300 300 1950 13200;
B 300 300 11750 13800;
B 300 300 11750 13200;
B 300 300 12550 17450;
B 300 300 1150 17450;
L M2;
B 10900 10900 6850 5500;
W 700 4650 10550 4650 15550;
L VI;
B 300 300 4650 14850;
B 300 300 4650 15550;
B 300 300 1750 10600;
B 300 300 1750 400;
B 300 300 11950 400;
B 300 300 11950 10600;
L GZ;
B 10000 10000 6850 5500;
L TX;
L DRC;
DF;
DS 5 1 1;
9 bcell.k;
L PW;
L AA;
B 3200 7300 26700 11350;
B 6500 7300 20350 11350;
B 3200 5100 26700 3650;

B 6500 5100 20350 3650;
B 3200 7300 2700 11350;
B 6500 7300 9050 11350;
B 3200 5100 2700 3650;
B 6500 5100 9050 3650;
L PY;
B 12000 300 6700 13550;
B 12000 300 6700 9150;
B 12000 300 6700 11350;
B 13400 700 6700 6950;
B 13400 700 6700 350;
B 12000 300 6700 2550;
B 12000 300 6700 4750;
B 700 700 350 13550;
B 700 700 350 11350;
B 700 700 350 9150;
B 700 700 350 2550;
B 700 700 350 4750;
B 12000 300 22700 13550;
B 12000 300 22700 9150;
B 12000 300 22700 11350;
B 13400 700 22700 6950;
B 12000 300 22700 2550;
B 12000 300 22700 4750;
B 700 700 29050 13550;
B 700 700 29050 11350;
B 700 700 29050 9150;
B 700 700 29050 2550;
B 700 700 29050 4750;
B 700 700 16350 13550;
B 700 700 16350 11350;
B 700 700 16350 9150;
B 700 700 16350 4750;
B 700 700 16350 2550;
B 700 700 13050 13550;
B 700 700 13050 11350;
B 700 700 13050 9150;
B 700 700 13050 4750;
B 700 700 13050 2550;
B 13400 700 22700 350;
L NI;
B 3700 5600 26700 3650;
B 3700 7800 2700 11350;
B 3700 5600 2700 3650;
B 3700 7800 26700 11350;
L PI;

B 7000 5600 20350 3650;
B 7000 5600 9050 3650;
B 7000 7800 20350 11350;
B 7000 7800 9050 11350;
L M1;
B 700 700 350 13550;
B 700 700 350 11350;
B 700 700 350 9150;
B 700 700 350 6950;
B 700 700 350 2550;
B 700 700 350 4750;
B 700 700 29050 13550;
B 700 700 29050 11350;
B 700 700 29050 9150;
B 700 700 29050 6950;
B 700 700 29050 2550;
B 700 700 29050 4750;
B 700 700 16350 13550;
B 700 700 16350 11350;
B 700 700 16350 9150;
B 700 700 17450 14650;
B 700 700 23250 14650;
B 700 700 25450 14650;
B 700 700 27950 14650;
B 700 700 23250 10250;
B 700 700 23250 12450;
B 700 700 25450 10250;
B 700 700 25450 12450;
B 700 700 27950 10250;
B 700 700 27950 12450;
B 700 700 17450 12450;
B 700 700 17450 10250;
B 700 700 17450 8050;
B 700 700 23250 8050;
B 700 700 25450 8050;
B 700 700 27950 8050;
B 700 700 16350 6950;
B 700 700 23250 3650;
B 700 700 23250 5850;
B 700 700 25450 3650;
B 700 700 25450 5850;
B 700 700 27950 3650;
B 700 700 27950 5850;
B 700 700 17450 5850;
B 700 700 17450 3650;
B 700 700 16350 4750;

B 700 700 16350 2550;
B 700 700 17450 1450;
B 700 700 23250 1450;
B 700 700 25450 1450;
B 700 700 27950 1450;
B 700 700 13050 13550;
B 700 700 13050 11350;
B 700 700 13050 9150;
B 700 700 11950 14650;
B 700 700 6150 14650;
B 700 700 3950 14650;
B 700 700 1450 14650;
B 700 700 6150 10250;
B 700 700 6150 12450;
B 700 700 3950 10250;
B 700 700 3950 12450;
B 700 700 1450 10250;
B 700 700 1450 12450;
B 700 700 11950 12450;
B 700 700 11950 10250;
B 700 700 11950 8050;
B 700 700 6150 8050;
B 700 700 3950 8050;
B 700 700 1450 8050;
B 700 700 13050 6950;
B 700 700 6150 3650;
B 700 700 6150 5850;
B 700 700 3950 3650;
B 700 700 3950 5850;
B 700 700 1450 3650;
B 700 700 1450 5850;
B 700 700 11950 5850;
B 700 700 11950 3650;
B 700 700 13050 4750;
B 700 700 13050 2550;
B 700 700 11950 1450;
B 700 700 6150 1450;
B 700 700 3950 1450;
B 700 700 1450 1450;
B 700 700 350 350;
B 700 700 29050 350;
B 700 700 16350 350;
B 700 700 16350 350;
B 700 700 13050 350;
L CC;
B 300 300 350 13550;

B 300 300 350 11350;
B 300 300 350 9150;
B 300 300 350 6950;
B 300 300 350 2550;
B 300 300 350 4750;
B 300 300 29050 13550;
B 300 300 29050 11350;
B 300 300 29050 9150;
B 300 300 29050 6950;
B 300 300 29050 2550;
B 300 300 29050 4750;
B 300 300 16350 13550;
B 300 300 16350 11350;
B 300 300 16350 9150;
B 300 300 17450 14650;
B 300 300 23250 14650;
B 300 300 25450 14650;
B 300 300 27950 14650;
B 300 300 23250 10250;
B 300 300 23250 12450;
B 300 300 25450 10250;
B 300 300 25450 12450;
B 300 300 27950 10250;
B 300 300 27950 12450;
B 300 300 17450 12450;
B 300 300 17450 10250;
B 300 300 17450 8050;
B 300 300 23250 8050;
B 300 300 25450 8050;
B 300 300 27950 8050;
B 300 300 16350 6950;
B 300 300 23250 3650;
B 300 300 23250 5850;
B 300 300 25450 3650;
B 300 300 25450 5850;
B 300 300 27950 3650;
B 300 300 27950 5850;
B 300 300 17450 5850;
B 300 300 17450 3650;
B 300 300 16350 4750;
B 300 300 16350 2550;
B 300 300 17450 1450;
B 300 300 23250 1450;
B 300 300 25450 1450;
B 300 300 27950 1450;
B 300 300 13050 13550;

APPENDIX 3:
Micro circuit
engineering BX software

A3.1 Introduction

The software consists of two packages: the BX Design and BX Layout software. For schematic entry only the first package is required and may be run on an IBM (or clone) personal computer. If layout is to be undertaken then a more expensive workstation such as Apollo Domain is required.

The BX software allows the design and layout of gate array and standard cell ASICs.

The information below has been supplied by Micro Circuit Engineering, Ashchurch, Tewkesbury, Gloucestershire, England.

A3.2 BX design software

The Design package consists of: Schematic Capture, Simulation, Timing Verification, Graphical waveform display and various analysis utilities.

A3.2.1 Schematic capture

This utility allows the user to enter the desired digital circuit in a familiar schematic form and compile the resulting graphics file into a design database suitable for simulation and subsequent layout and pattern generator tape generation. It features all the facilities one might expect, e.g. multiple sheet drawing area, 'rubber banding', names nodes, color display on most machines, mouse driven, snap to connection, hierarchical structure. The latter, along with the use of zero delay input/output pads, allows a top-down approach by enabling the user to validate modular parts of the design before inclusion at a higher level. It also allows a user to build up a library of customized macro functions. There are currently three libraries available: 5-micron, 3-micron and standard cell—all CMOS.

A3.2.2 Simulation and timing verification

The simulator is an event driven, 6-state, lumped delay simulator that is particularly efficient because it is designed to simulate MCE's own family of devices. Hierarchical designs are flattened and the delay at each node is modelled as the delay through the gate in question plus the additional delay due to the inputs connected to that node. Full hierarchy is supported. In timing verification mode, checks are made on various primitive cells that require stated timing parameters to be met, i.e. setup and hold times on flip-flops, node contention for tristate cells, etc.

With an eye to the future task of production, the waveform description language, without sacrificing flexibility for circuit validation, is biased toward what can be achieved with automatic test equipment. If certain conventions and rules are adhered to, customer-generated waveforms can be translated into a functional test program with a minimum of work.

The simulator control language is both simple and effective and allows the user to influence the operation of the simulator in the following ways:

Check mode
This enables the predicted output states to be checked against actual outputs obtained during simulation.

Delay scaling
This feature allows the nominal propagation delays contained in the library to be scaled by a user-defined multiplication factor. In this way it is possible to evaluate the effects of voltage and temperature on the performance of the design. Through much experience and corroborative measurement, MCE has found that designs functioning satisfactorily over a range from 0.3 to 1.7 scaling factor are suitable for military screened products.

Monitoring facilities
Any node in the circuit may be monitored including input/output pads and hierarchically qualified nodes. Those points monitored will result in a printed line of output from the simulator each time that node changes state. This information may also be built into a results file suitable for display by a graphical waveform display program. There is also the ability to turn the monitor on and off during simulation of sections of no interest, so as to limit the amount of output data to that which is relevant.

A3.2.3 Design database analysis

Design database analysis is achieved with two utilities:

1. a delay program that tabulates minimum and maximum unloaded and loaded delays and the loading factor for each node in the circuit; and
2. a program that gives statistical details about the number of types of cells and input/output pads used and the percentage utilization for various chip sizes.

A3.2.4 Waveform database analysis

There are also two utilities to aid analysis of the waveform database; one displays the waveform file in a truth table format and the other gives statistical data on the number of test cycles and the number of vectors used and a check of waveform activity at the output pads.

A3.3 BX layout software

Once a design database has been validated, the BX Layout software is used to lay the design out and prepare pattern generator information. The suite consists of: placement and routing, graphical editing, via reduction, and checking utilities.

A3.3.1 Placement strategies

Placement can be manual, automatic or a combination of both. Generally at least the input/output pads positions are defined then the remainder of the cells are auto-placed. There are three placement strategies to choose from.

Placement Strategy 1
This approach has three stages to it. First, it decides which cells will be in which row on the basis of a min-cut algorithm, i.e. it keeps to a minimum the number of connections from row to row. Second, each row is treated separately and the cells placed along the row, again using a min-cut approach within the row. Finally a relaxation technique is applied to optimize the placement cells within a row with respect to connections to adjacent rows. This strategy tends to produce very dense layouts.

Placement Strategy 2
This strategy is the same as strategy 1 but the cells are temporarily enlarged in size, placed as above, then shrunk back to their correct size. The impact of this strategy is to spread the design out over the available cell area leaving room between cells. This can be a desirable approach when the design has many connections traversing the chip and thus requiring connections through the active areas.

Placement Strategy 3
This approach is only applicable if a hierarchical design approach has been adopted. The algorithm groups cells together in the same way that they have been used in the hierarchy of the circuit definition and tries to place them together. The success of this technique is largely dependant on how the circuit was partitioned to begin with.

The placement program adds the placement data to the design database and outputs a file listing the cell locations as a grid reference on the array. This is also updated if editing is subsequently performed.

A3.3.2 Routing

Generally, routing is done automatically though it can be done manually. There are six stages. The first stage builds a point to point connection matrix (birds nest) based on the placement data. The next stage takes crossing signals and swops these if this is possible while maintaining functionality, e.g. swopping the inputs of a 3-input NAND gate. The router then routes those signals that can be routed within the cells. The fourth stage is to allocate connections to the routing channels on a congestion basis, swopping signals from one side of the cell (most cells have the same connections top and bottom) to the other and introducing interchannel interconnects (known as 2INTS). This is known as pre-placing segments. Channel routing is the next stage where the pre-placed segments are routed in. In the final stage a maze router tries to complete the remaining unrouted segments.

A3.3.3 Editing

Inevitably, either some designs will not be completely routed or the resulting layout is in some way unsatisfactory, thus requiring some manual editing. Micro Circuit Engineering's experience with the FALCON service has shown that if certain basic design rules are observed, then the vast majority of designs can be auto-placed and routed with a minimum of effort spent on manual intervention.

The layout editor allows the designer to view the resulting design on a color terminal and modify or complete the routing. It displays both the whole chip and a user definable magnified area of the chip in separate windows. There is also a menu area and a window for messages. The salient features are the ability to:

1. delete and add metal routing tracks;
2. place and move primitive cells from the validated design database both individually and in blocks;
3. place and delete inter-channel interconnect cells;
4. highlight the path of an identified network node;
5. find unplaced segments;
6. check the laid out design against the design database for correspondence of connectivity and other errors such as shorts to power rails, etc.; and
7. restore the layout to the state at the last check.

A3.3.4 Via reduction

Once the circuit has been completely routed to the satisfaction of the designer a 'via reduction' program may be run which shorts out all used polysilicon underpasses that have no metal passing over them.

A3.3.5 Design checks

Design checking consists of two programs. The first stage takes the completed design and translates it into polygon data and checks both geometric design rules (DRC checks) and electrical design rules (ERC checks) then extracts a network list from the polygon data. The second program compares the extracted net list against a master copy of the original validated net list to ensure connectivity has been maintained.

A3.4 Post-layout simulation

Post-layout simulation is clearly necessary to evaluate the effect of interconnect on critical signals, but more subtle is the effect of signal slowing. The assumption when simulating pre-layout is that all inputs being driven by a given output change stage at the same time. In reality, since the layout of the same node might be 'tree like' in shape and involve different delay routes to different inputs, then the signal arriving at these inputs may well be staggered and hence unexpected glitches and spikes could be generated.

Post-layout simulation is achieved by first extracting interconnect data from the laid out design. This takes the form of both segments of metal tracking and lengths of polysilicon as well as interchannel interconnects. The interconnection routes are then modeled as RC transmission networks and the response to a step input analyzed. The additional delays incurred are then updated into the design database which may then be simulated in the normal manner.

Micro Circuit Engineering has found that, for 5-micron designs, post-layout simulation is not always necessary for prototypes, if certain simple design rules are adhered to.

Index